The Complete
Rock & Pop
Guitar Player

by Mick Barker, Rick Cardinali, Roger Day.

Books 1, 2 & 3

Omnibus Edition

Wise Publications
London/New York/Paris/Sydney/Copenhagen/Madrid

The Fret Board

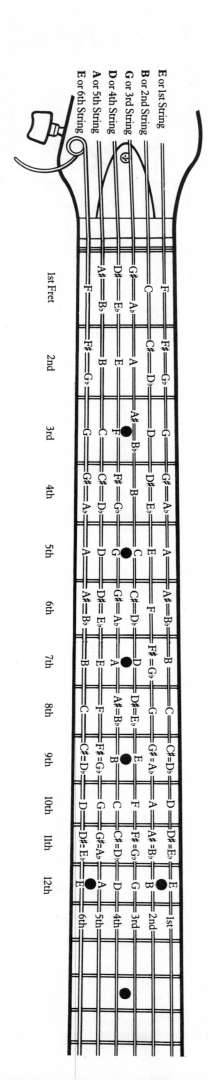

Book 1

Book 2

Book 3

Introduction

This course will help you to realise your ambition to play rock and pop in the style of your favourite stars. With its special simplified system of notation you need no previous knowledge of music or of the guitar.

The songs are carefully graded and when you have finished the course you will move on easily to reading conventional musical notation. The course is equally suitable for classroom or private use.

Book 1
Holding, tuning the guitar. Chord changing. Play like Bruce Springsteen . . . Wings.

Book 2
Tablature, backing riffs, rock and reggae. Play along with Eric Clapton . . . The Rolling Stones.

Book 3
Harmony, arpeggios, strumming effects, modern rhythm styles. Great songs by Status Quo . . . Stevie Wonder.

By the end of this course you will have become the complete rock and pop player.

The Complete
Rock & Pop
Guitar Player

by Mick Barker, Rick Cardinali, Roger Day.

Book 1

Songs and music in this book

The Guitar

Whether you have an acoustic or an electric guitar, the principles of playing are fundamentally the same, and so are most of the features on both instruments. In order to 'electrify' an acoustic guitar (as in the diagram), a magnetic pick-up can be attached to those guitars with steel strings or a 'bug' style microphone pick-up can be attached to guitars with nylon strings. If in doubt check with your local music shop.

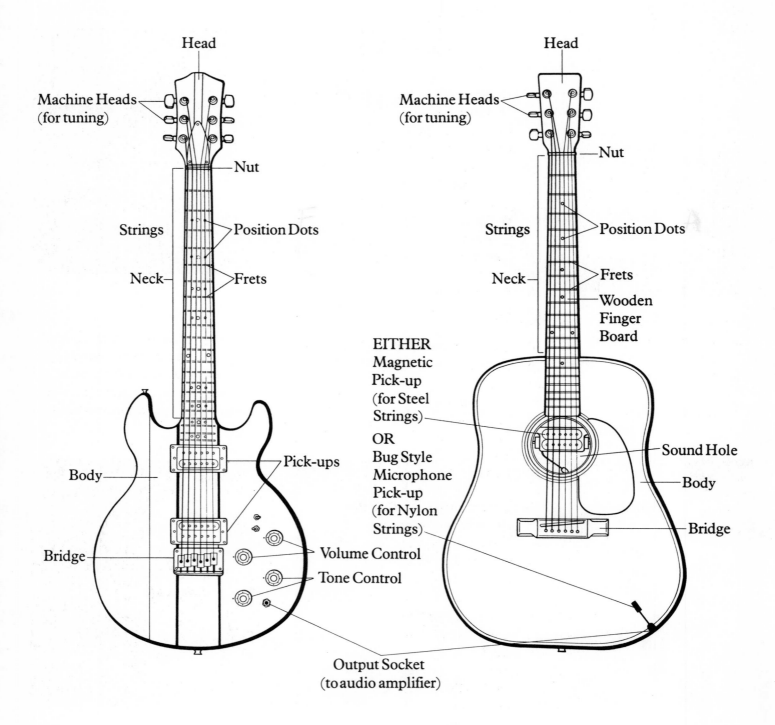

Head

Machine Heads (for tuning)

Nut

Strings

Position Dots

Neck

Frets

Body

Pick-ups

Bridge

Volume Control

Tone Control

Output Socket (to audio amplifier)

Head

Machine Heads (for tuning)

Nut

Strings

Position Dots

Neck

Frets

Wooden Finger Board

EITHER Magnetic Pick-up (for Steel Strings)

OR Bug Style Microphone Pick-up (for Nylon Strings)

Sound Hole

Body

Bridge

Holding The Guitar

The picture above shows a comfortable position for playing rock or pop guitar

The Right Hand

When STRUMMING (brushing your fingers across the strings), hold your fingers together.

When PICKING (plucking strings individually), hold your wrist further away from the strings than for strumming. Keep your thumb slightly to the left of your fingers which should be above the three treble strings as shown.

The Plectrum

Many modern guitar players prefer to use a plectrum to strike the strings. Plectrums come in many sizes, shapes and thicknesses and all are available from your local music shop. Start with a fairly large, soft one if possible, with a grip. The photo shows the correct way to hold your plectrum.

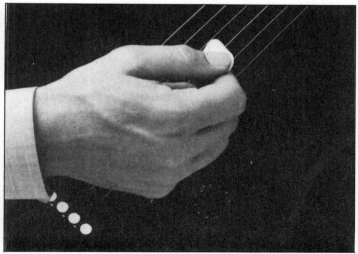

Left Hand

Use your finger tips to press down the strings in the positions described in this book. Your thumb should be behind your 1st and 2nd fingers pressing on the middle of the back of the neck.

Tuning

Accurate tuning of the guitar is essential and is achieved by winding the machine heads up or down.
It is always better to tune 'up' to the correct pitch rather than down. Therefore,
if you find that the pitch of your string is higher (sharper) than the correct pitch,
you should 'wind' down below the correct pitch and *then* 'tune up' to it.

Relative Tuning

Tuning the guitar to itself without the aid of a pitch pipe or other tuning device.

Other Methods of Tuning

Pitch pipe
Tuning fork
Dedicated electronic guitar tuner

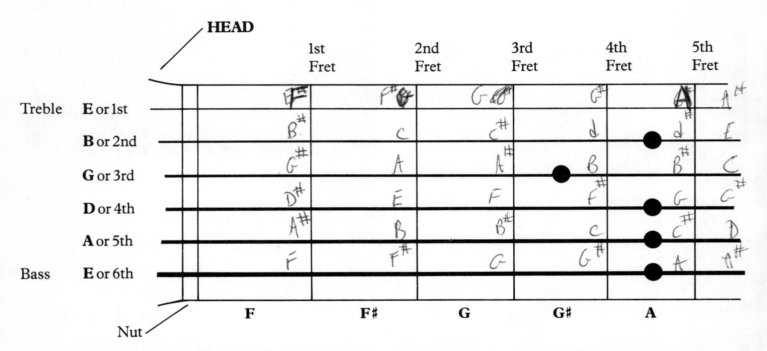

Press down where indicated, one at a time, following the instructions below.

Estimate the pitch of the 6th string as near as possible to **E** or at least a comfortable pitch (not too high, as you might break other strings in tuning up).

Then, while checking the various positions on the above diagram, place a finger from your left hand on:

the 5th fret of the E or 6th string and **tune the open A** (or 5th string) to the note (A)

the 5th fret of the A or 5th string and **tune the open D** (or 4th string) to the note (D)

the 5th fret of the D or 4th string and **tune the open G** (or 3rd string) to the note (G)

the 4th fret of the G or 3rd string and **tune the open B** (or 2nd string) to the note (B)

the 5th fret of the B or 2nd string and **tune the open E** (or 1st string) to the note (E)

4

Chord Boxes

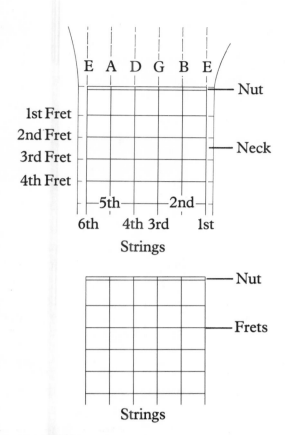

The **A** Chord.

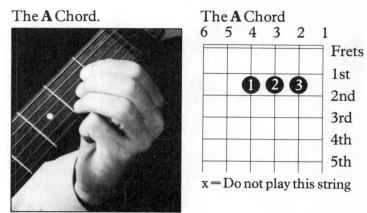

The **A** Chord

x = Do not play this string

All chords are major chords unless otherwise indicated.

Left Hand

Place all three fingers into position and press down firmly. Keep your thumb around the middle back of the neck and directly behind your 1st and 2nd fingers.

CHORD BOXES are diagrams of the guitar neck viewed head upwards, face on, as illustrated in the above drawings. The horizontal double line at the top is the nut, the other horizontal lines are the frets. The vertical lines are the strings starting from E or 6th on the left to E or 1st on the right.

Any dots with numbers inside them simply indicate which finger goes where. Any strings marked with an X must not be played.

The fingers of your hand are numbered 1,2,3, & 4 as in the diagram below.

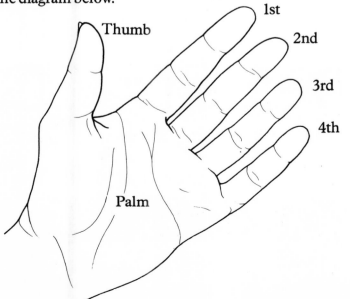

Right Hand Thumb or Plectrum

Slowly play each string, starting with the 5th or A string and moving up to the 1st or E string. IF THERE IS ANY BUZZING, PERHAPS YOU NEED TO:–
Position your fingers nearer the metal fret (towards you);
or adjust the angle of your hand;
 or check that the buzz is not elsewhere on the guitar by playing the open strings in the same manner.

Finally, your nails may be too long, in which case, you are pressing down at an extreme angle and therefore not firmly enough. Also, the pad of one of your fingers may be in the way of the next string for the same reason.

So cut your nails to a more comfortable length and then try to keep them as near vertical to the fretboard as possible.

Once you have a 'buzz free' sound, play the chord a few times and then remove your fingers and repeat the exercise until your positioning is right instinctively.

Now turn the page.

Mull of Kintyre

Words and Music: McCartney/Laine

The **D** Chord

The **D** Chord

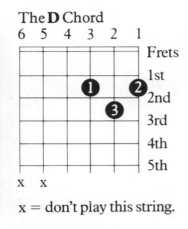

x = don't play this string.

Place your fingers in the correct positions and press down firmly. Remember to keep your thumb around the middle back of the neck and directly behind your 1st and 2nd fingers.

Then follow the same procedure as you did for the **A** chord. This time starting from the 4th (D) string.

Now, are you able to play both chords clearly and cleanly every time? GOOD.

Next, hold down the **A** chord and, keeping the fingers of your *right hand* together, brush your nails down the

strings from bass **A** (or 5th string) to the treble **E** (or 1st string). Alternatively do the same thing holding your plectrum as shown previously. Then strum this rhythm using down strokes, signified by a downward arrow. Try to keep your strums evenly spaced.

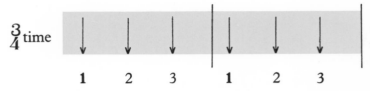

Well, if you want to sound technical, you can say you have just played your first two bars of 3/4 time.

Basically, '3/4 (three-four) time' means three beats in a bar, these bars are separated by a bar line which means the end of one bar and the beginning of another.

Now, still holding down your **A** chord, practise changing to **D** with your 'three in a bar' rhythm, this time accentuating the first strum of every bar. It is best to play slowly and evenly at first, so that you have time to change chords without stopping.

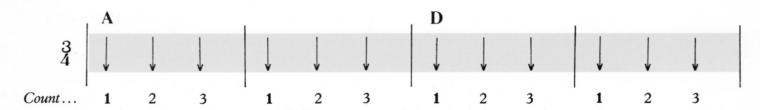

Take note that, at the beginning of the last line of music for this song, you will see the letter 'E'. At this stage, simply strike the bass 'E' or 6th string once, and let the open string sound or 'ring' for the 3 beats of that bar.

Later on in the book you will be given the 'E' chord, which you can substitute for the single note 'E' once you have progressed to that stage.

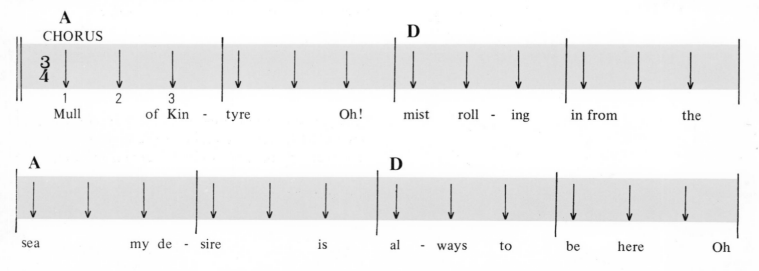

6

Mull of Kintyre Continued

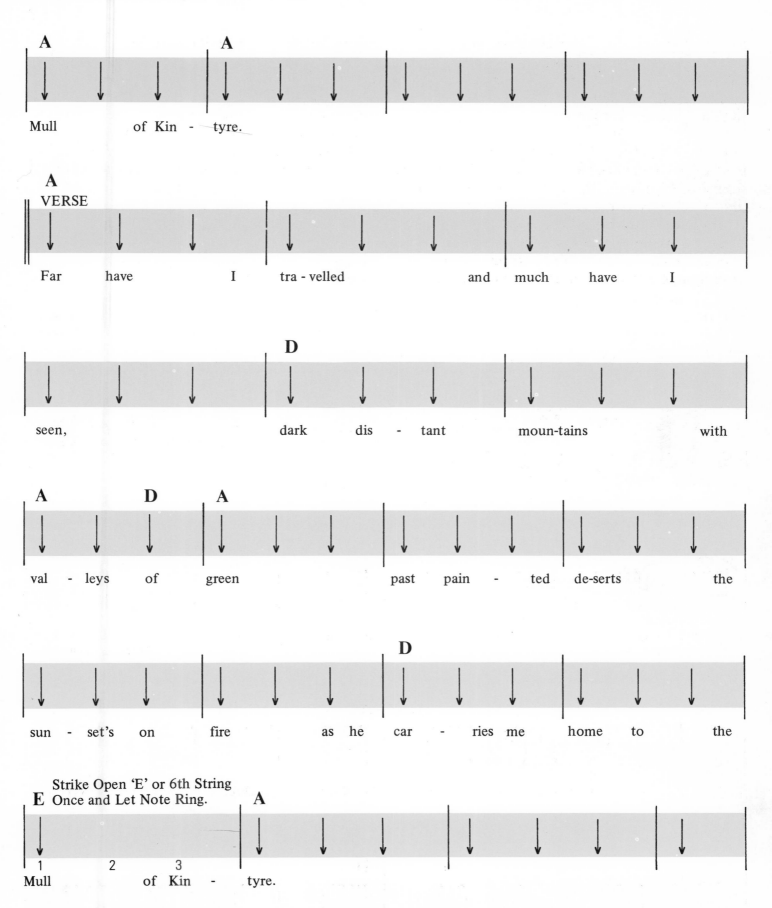

N.B. The full lyric for each song can be found at the back of the book.

Tom Hark

Music: R. Bopape. New Lyrics: Bob Grover

Now it's time for you to learn your second tune. It's a piece which was a smash hit for The Piranhas and is called 'Tom Hark'. You don't need to learn any new chords for this tune but you are going to learn a new strumming pattern.

The first piece you learnt, 'Mull Of Kintyre', was played in Waltz or 3/4 time and has 3 beats in each bar with one strum for each beat. 'Tom Hark' has 4 beats to each bar (this is called 4/4 time) and we're going to play two strums for each beat. If you look at the first bar you'll see 1 & 2 etc. written under the words. Tap your foot four times in each bar and on the first tap count '1 &', on the second tap count '2 &' and so on. The number is the down stroke and the '&' is the up stroke.

There's only one more thing to learn and then you can get on with playing the song. This piece of music is written in a swing or shuffle style which means you make the down stroke long and the up stroke short (long and short in this instance refer to time not distance). Try it over a few times and you'll see what is meant.

N.B. For those with some musical knowledge the strums could have been written ⌐⌐ etc. – but that will be explained in later books.

SWING/SHUFFLE

Repeat 4 times

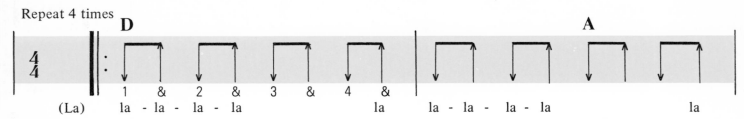

(La) la - la - la - la   la   la - la - la - la   la

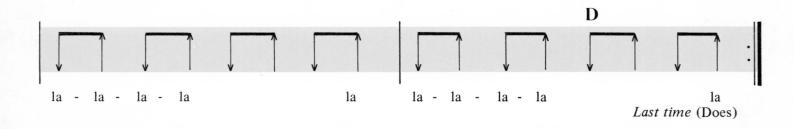

la - la - la - la   la   la - la - la - la   la

Last time (Does)

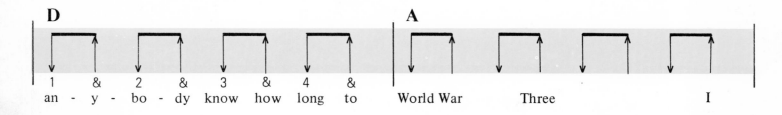

an - y - bo - dy know how long to   World War   Three   I

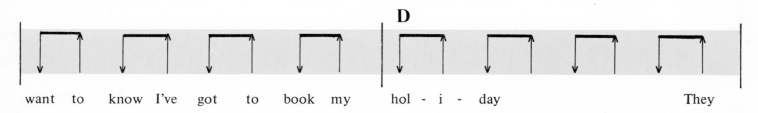

want   to   know I've got   to   book   my   hol - i - day   They

Tom Hark Continued

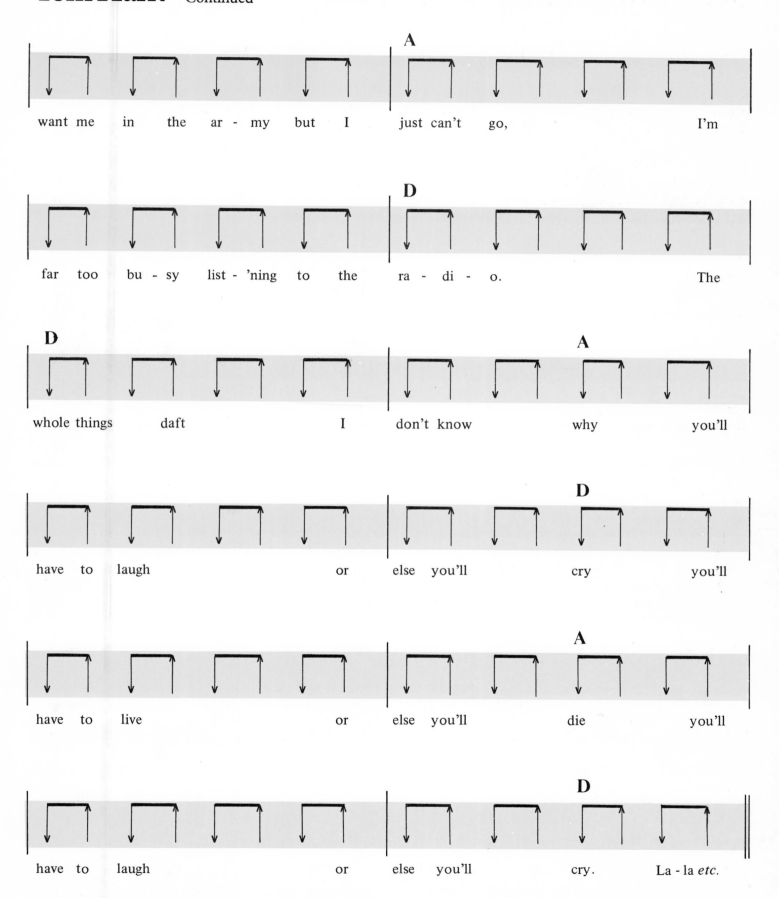

A
want me in the ar - my but I just can't go, I'm

D
far too bu - sy list - 'ning to the ra - di - o. The

D   A
whole things daft I don't know why you'll

                                                     D
have to laugh or else you'll cry you'll

                                                     A
have to live or else you'll die you'll

                                                     D
have to laugh or else you'll cry. La - la *etc.*

N.B. The full lyric for each song can be found at the back of the book.

Summertime Blues

Words & Music: Eddie Cochran & Jerry Capehart

The E Chord

The E Chord

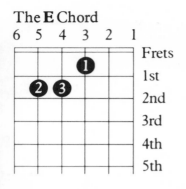

Now you are going to learn your first six-string chord, the chord of **E**. We're going to use it in that classic rock 'n' roll song 'Summertime Blues', originally recorded by Eddie Cochran.

Study the chord box and photo and try playing the chord. As always, play each string separately at first to make sure each note is sounding clearly. Then try strumming full up and down strokes.

Each time you learn a new chord it is a good idea to practise changing smoothly between all the chords you know.

A very good tip: when changing from **E** to **D** or **D** to **E** don't take all your fingers off the strings. The first finger can slide up and down between the first and second frets and makes a good reference point. Try it and you'll see what is meant.

This is not a shuffle song like 'Tom Hark'. Although the timing of the strum pattern looks the same, make all the strokes even. This is called 'straight eight style', because there are eight even strums to a bar.

Finally, in the short instrumental sections notice what a different sound you get by playing four down strokes followed by two up and down strokes. It may take a little practice but it's well worth it. O.K., now you're ready to sing along with Eddie Cochran and 'Summertime Blues'.

STRAIGHT EIGHTS

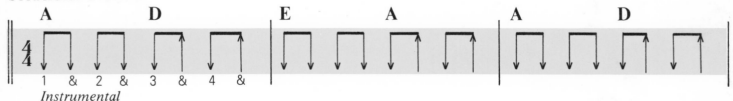

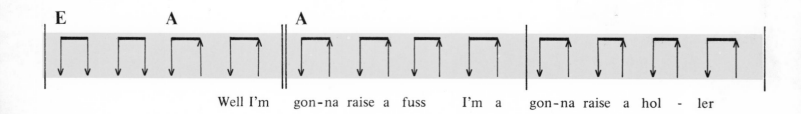

Well I'm gon-na raise a fuss   I'm a   gon-na raise a hol-ler

Summertime Blues Continued

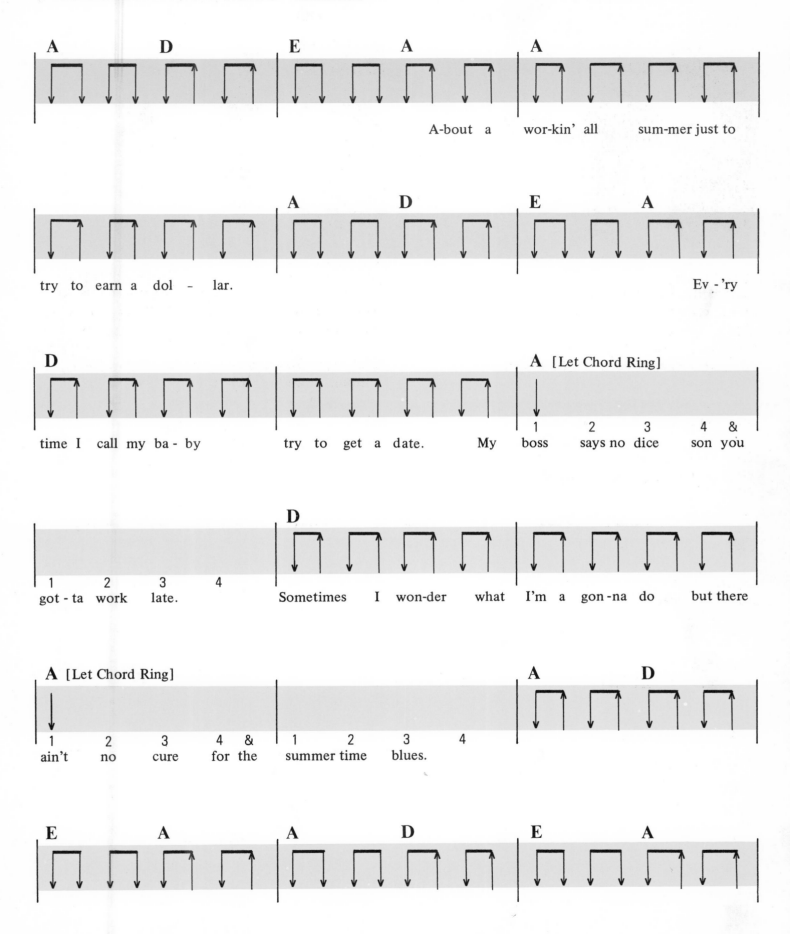

N.B. The full lyric for each song can be found at the back of the book.

Hello I Love You

Words & Music: The Doors

The **G** Chord

The **G** Chord

The **C** Chord

The **C** Chord

To play the **G** chord, start by placing your 1st finger on the 2nd fret of the 5th string and then locate the other finger positions.

For the **C** chord, start by placing your 1st finger on the 1st fret of the 2nd string and then locate the other positions.

Remember to play only the top five strings and keep your fingers as near to vertical as possible, so that the pads of your fingers don't interfere with the ringing of adjacent strings.

'Hello I Love You' was a monster hit for the Doors, featuring the great Jim Morrison on vocals. The 'down up' strum pattern is easy to play and the vocals are easy to sing.

STRAIGHT EIGHTS

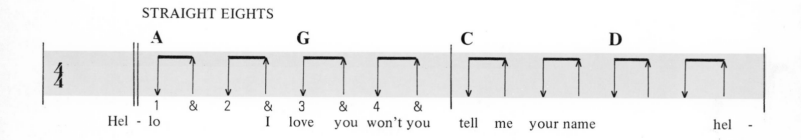

1 & 2 & 3 & 4 &
Hel - lo   I love you won't you   tell me your name   hel -

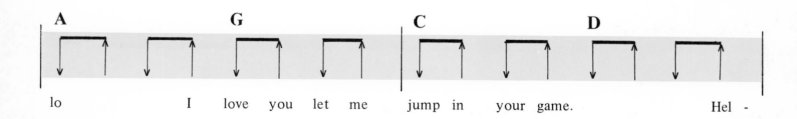

lo   I love you let me   jump in your game.   Hel -

Hello, I Love You Continued

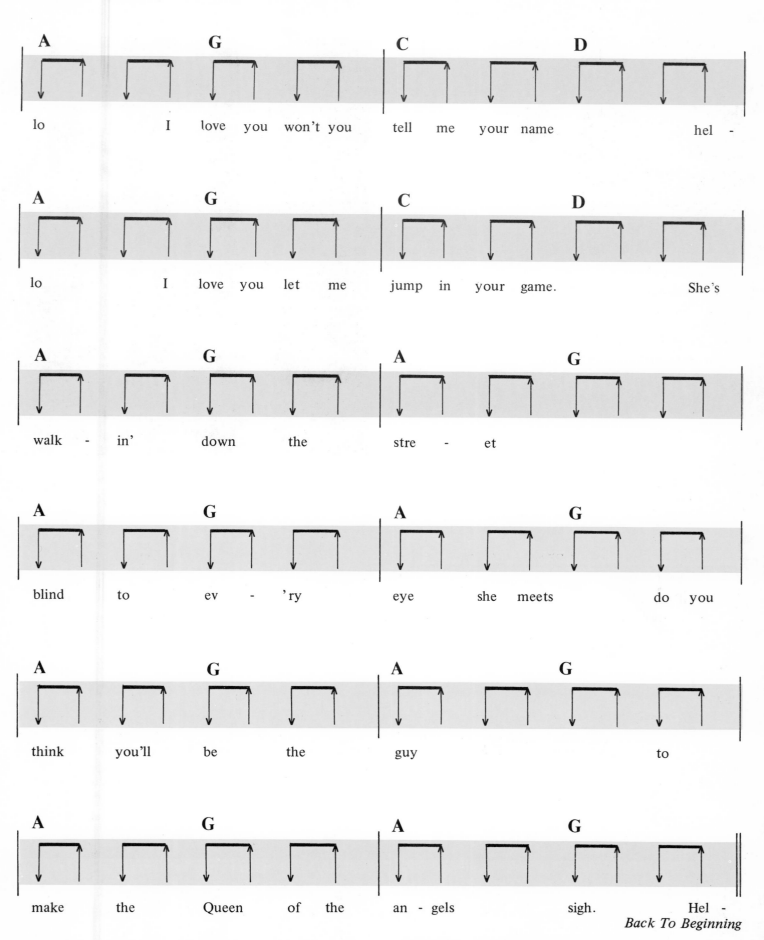

N.B. The full lyric for each song can be found at the back of the book.

Get Off Of My Cloud

Words & Music: Mick Jagger & Keith Richard

This was a big hit for The Rolling Stones and you don't have to learn any new chords to play it.

To get the right feel for this song, make the first and third beats of each bar heavier than the others. In almost every bar the chord changes on the first and third beats so you'll find it very easy to play.

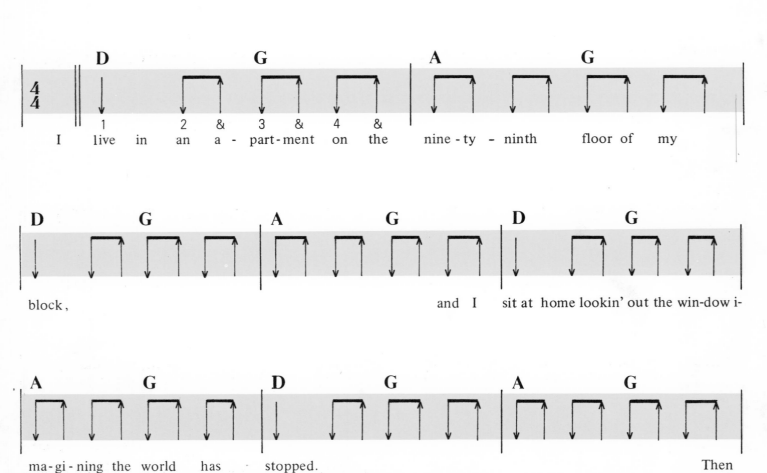

I live in an a-part-ment on the nine-ty-ninth floor of my

block, and I sit at home lookin' out the win-dow i-

ma-gi-ning the world has stopped. Then

Get Off Of My Cloud
Continued

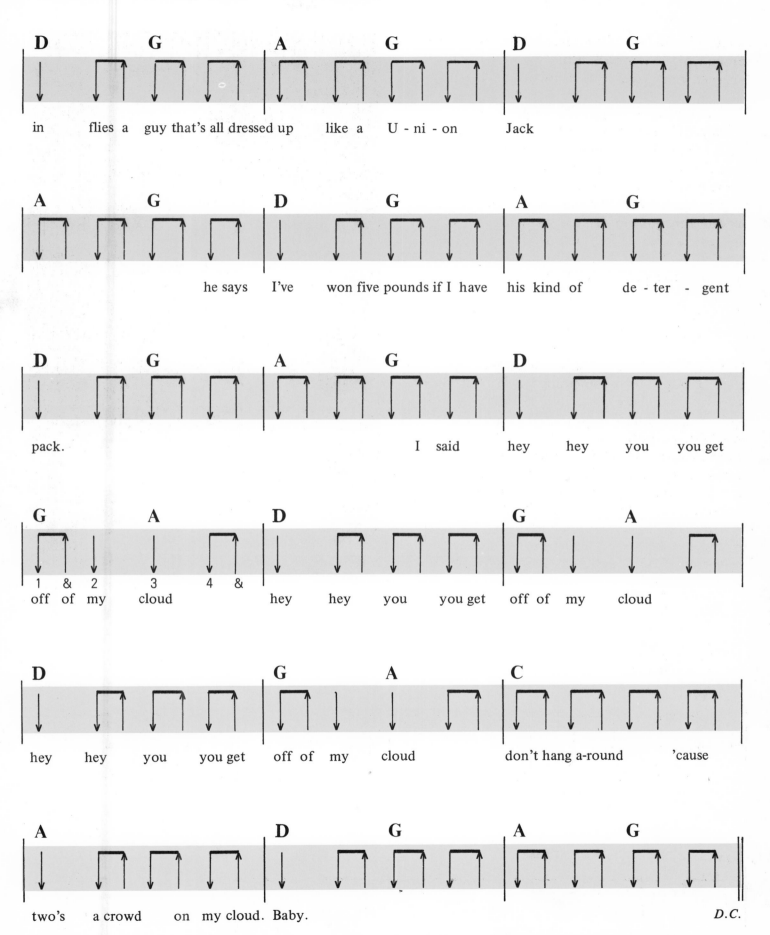

in flies a guy that's all dressed up like a U - ni - on Jack

he says I've won five pounds if I have his kind of de - ter - gent

pack. I said hey hey you you get

1 & 2 3 4 &
off of my cloud hey hey you you get off of my cloud

hey hey you you get off of my cloud don't hang a-round 'cause

two's a crowd on my cloud. Baby.

D.C.

N.B. The full lyric for each song can be found at the back of the book.

That'll Be The Day

Words & Music: Norman Petty, Buddy Holly, Jerry Allison

Again, the chords you have already learnt will see you through this famous rock 'n' roll standard. There are, however, some important new things to learn.

This song is played in the same swing-shuffle style which you learnt for 'Tom Hark' but there are a couple of important additions. First, look at the last bar of the verse. This very simple strum pattern is something you've heard hundreds of times on rock and pop records. Just tap your foot four times in the bar as usual but each time you tap your foot count 1,2,3 for each tap and strum as shown. Do you recognise the rhythm? Easy isn't it? Three notes played in the time of one are called triplets and are written  .

This will be explained fully in a later book. For the moment, you need not concern yourself with this.

The only other thing you have to learn before you start to play is how to leave something out. Look at the last two bars of the chorus. Two bars from the end you will notice a sign saying 'let chord ring'. This means that you should strum the first beat of the bar only, but let the chord sound for the full four beats. At the start of the last bar there is a small sign that has not been mentioned before, known as a 'rest'. This, too, will be explained more fully in a later book. It means that you don't play on the '1' of the bar. Start on the '&' with an upstroke as shown, and you'll be ready for the rest of the bar. As always, you'll soon recognise the phrase.

CHORUS
Swing/Shuffle

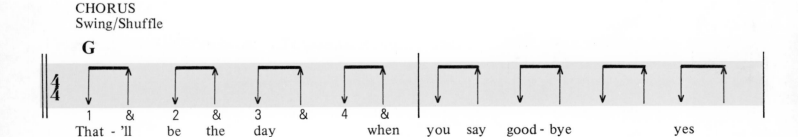

G

1 & 2 & 3 & 4 &
That - 'll be the day when you say good - bye yes

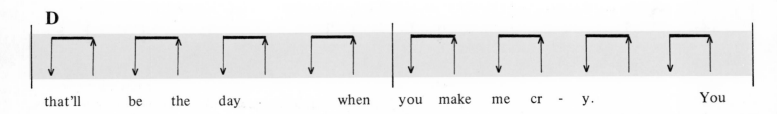

D

that'll be the day when you make me cr - y. You

16

That'll Be The Day Continued

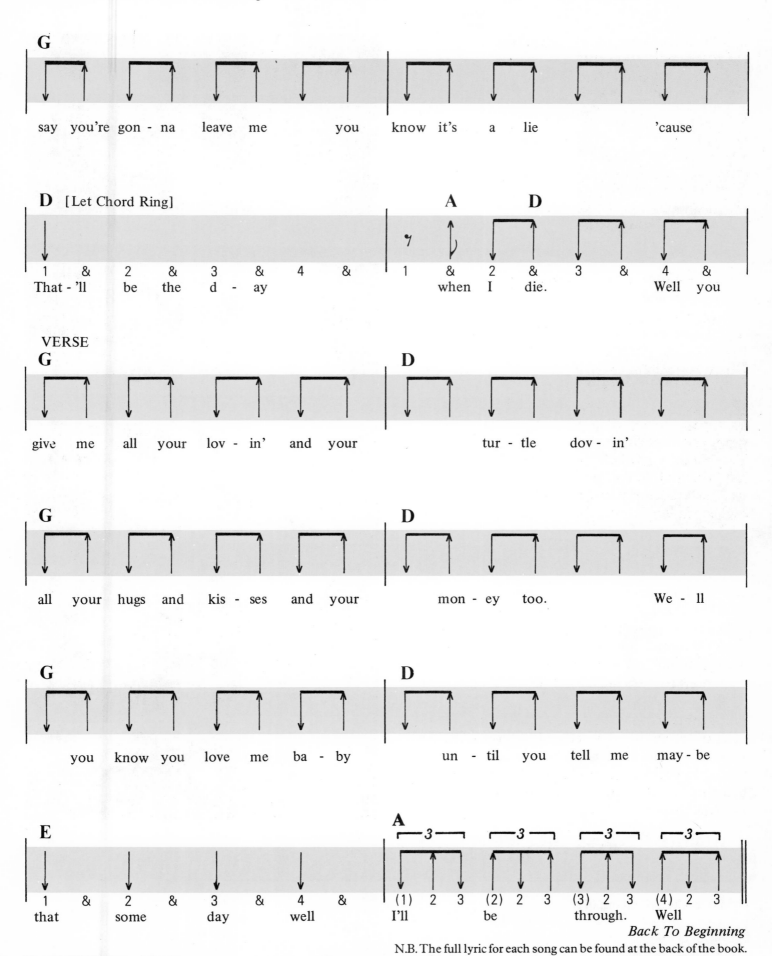

Back To Beginning
N.B. The full lyric for each song can be found at the back of the book.

Black Magic Woman   Words & Music: Peter Green

The D minor Chord

The Dm Chord

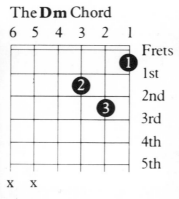

To play **D minor** place your 1st finger on the 1st fret of the 1st string and then locate the other positions.

The A minor Chord

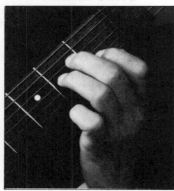

The A m Chord

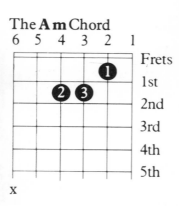

For **A minor** place your 1st finger on the 1st fret of the 2nd string and then locate the other positions. Practise changing between the two chords until you can do it clearly. Use a slow tempo to practise so that you don't have to stop for each change. Remember that playing evenly is the most important thing. You will notice that 'minor' chords have a sad sound and are often used by composers to give a melancholy feel to a song.

Finally, this little guitar figure is an important part of the song and occurs on the rest bar of each verse. So, for verse 1 you should start to play it as you sing the word 'me' at the beginning of the last bar. It is written out below in easy notation, with the appropriate excerpt from the lyric.

String	3		4		5			6	5
Fret	2	0	2	0	3	2	0	3	0

try'n to make a devil out of me

Black Magic Woman

Continued

STRAIGHT EIGHTS

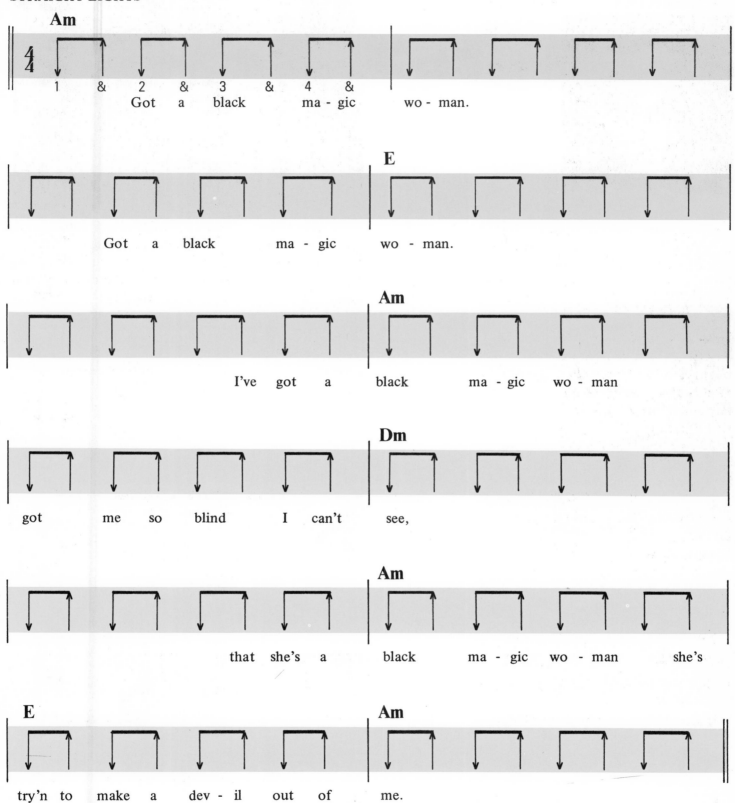

Am

4/4   1   &   2   &   3   &   4   &

Got   a   black   ma - gic   wo - man.

E

Got   a   black   ma - gic   wo - man.

Am

I've   got   a   black   ma - gic   wo - man

Dm

got   me   so   blind   I   can't   see,

Am

that   she's   a   black   ma - gic   wo - man   she's

E

try'n   to   make   a   dev - il   out   of

Am

me.

N.B. The full lyric for each song can be found at the back of the book.

Stand By Me

Words & Music: Ben E. King, Jerry Lieber and Mike Stoller

The **E minor** Chord

The **E m** Chord

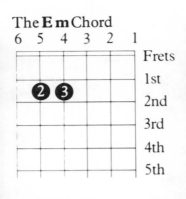

You learnt your first minor chords for the last song. Well, here's another one. It's called **E minor** and we're going to use it in this next song which, incidentally, has been a hit for several artists, including an outstanding version by John Lennon on his 'Rock 'n' Roll' album.

First, let's examine the new chord. You'll notice it's exactly the same as the **E** chord you have already learnt but without the first finger on the third string. There is an important 'musical reason' why this is so and we will talk about that in later books.

Up to now we have had a maximum of two strums per tap of the foot and we have been counting 1 & 2 & etc. for each tap. If you look at the first beat of each bar you will see there is an extra strum between the '&' sign and the '2'. Count this extra strum as an 'a'.

To recap, the rhythm of each bar is counted as 1 & a 2 & 3 & 4 &. Remember, you must arrive at the '2' on the second foot tap so you have to squeeze the 'a' strum in between the '&' and the '2'.

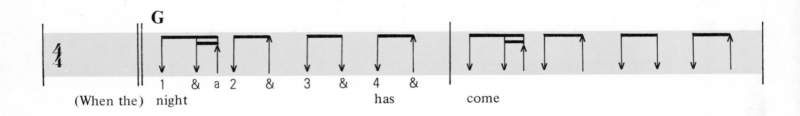

(When the) night ... has come

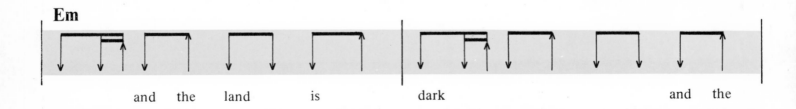

and the land is ... dark ... and the

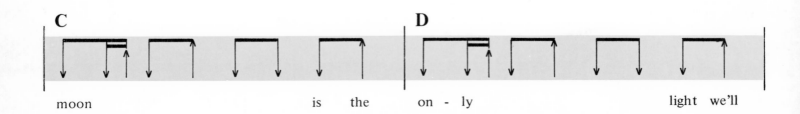

moon ... is the on-ly ... light we'll

Stand By Me Continued

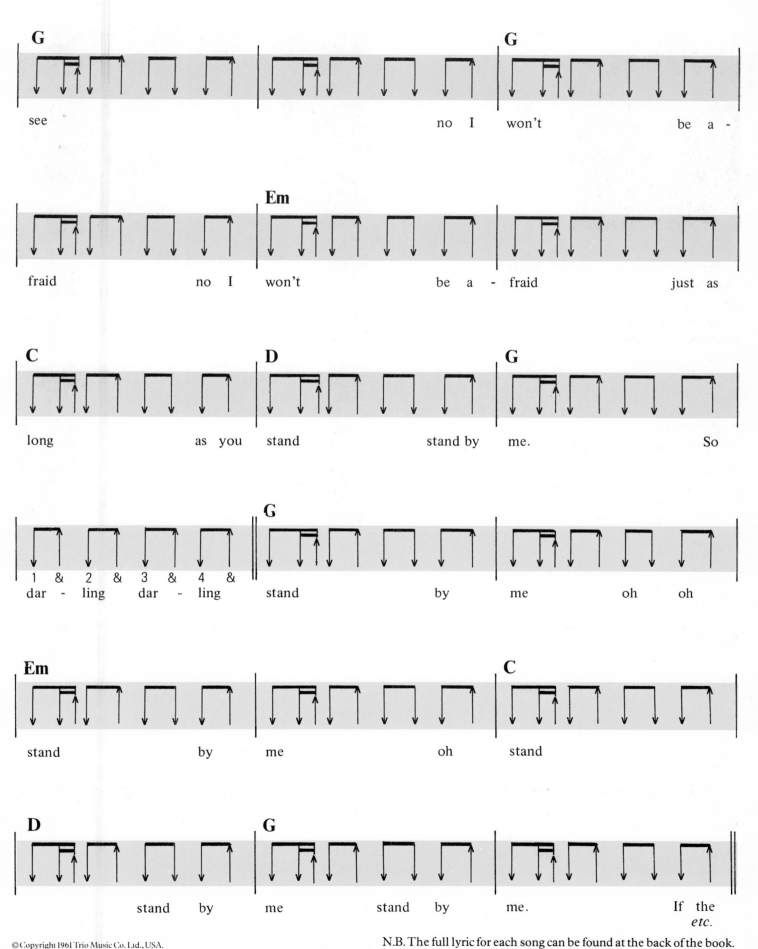

N.B. The full lyric for each song can be found at the back of the book.

Paint It Black

Words & Music: Mick Jagger & Keith Richard

The **E seventh** Chord

The **E 7** Chord

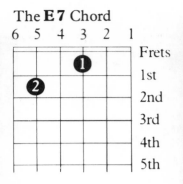

This new chord is very easy to play because you have already learnt the **E** chord for 'Summertime Blues'. All you have to do is place your fingers in the same position as for the **E** chord and simply remove your 3rd finger from the fretboard, and allow the open 4th (or D) string to sound. Remember to keep your fingers as near vertical to the fretboard as possible. You may find that if you are not careful the pad of your 2nd finger will interfere with the clear ringing of the open 4th string.

You will notice that the **E 7** chord has an 'expectant' sound, and goes well when played before **A** or **A minor.** It has been used by many artists as a lead-in chord to a song. Just strum **E 7** once letting it ring and you will understand what is meant.

STRAIGHT EIGHTS

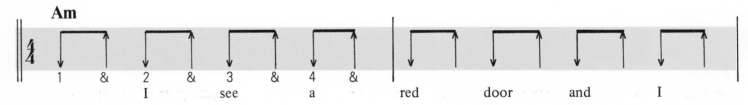

Am

| 1 | & | 2 | & | 3 | & | 4 | & | | red | door | and | I |
| I | | see | | a | | | | | | | | |

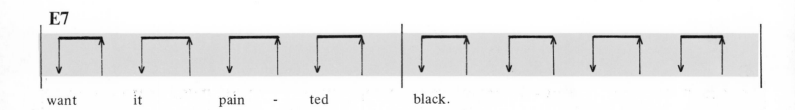

E7

want   it   pain - ted   black.

Paint It Black   Continued

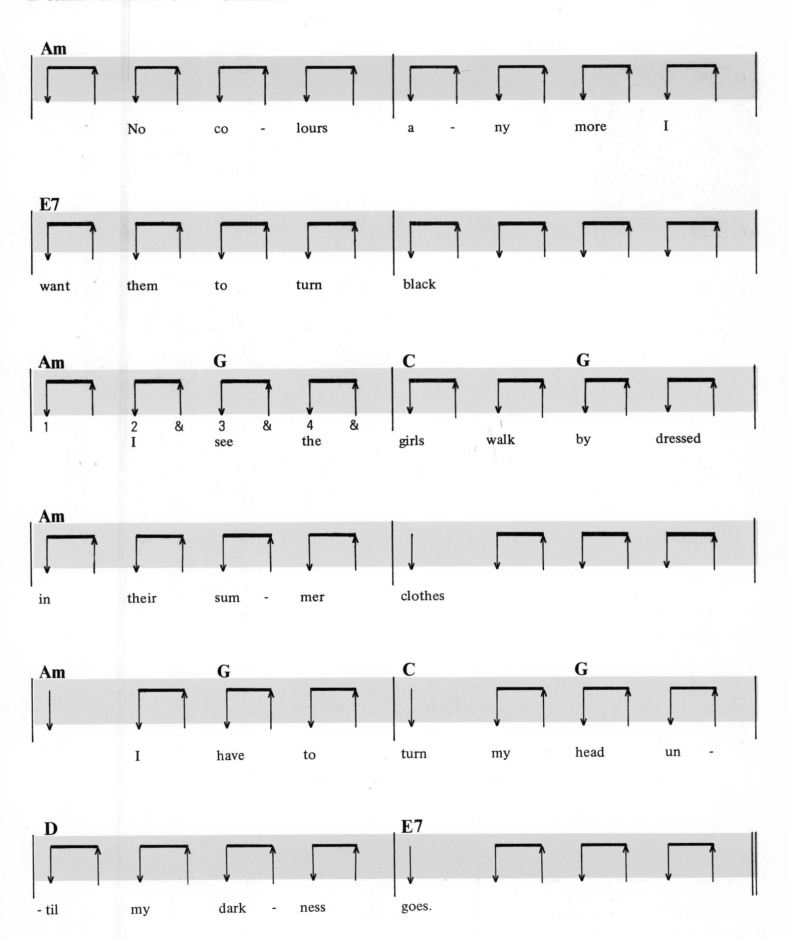

N.B. The full lyric for each song can be found at the back of the book.

Ob-La-Di   Words & Music: John Lennon and Paul McCartney

The G seventh Chord

The G 7 Chord

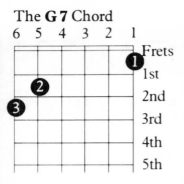

This big hit by Lennon and McCartney introduces another 7th chord. This is **G 7**. Unfortunately, it is not quite as easy to change **G** into **G 7** as it was to change **E** into **E 7** but by now you should not have any trouble with it.

What you must do is completely change the fingering between the two chords. Study the chord box for **G 7** and the earlier chord box for **G,** and you'll see what is meant.

Practise the change between these two chords and then we will talk about the strumming.

The pattern here is the 'straight eight' feel with which you should be familiar by now. The only difference is that you accent what is called the 'off beat'. The 'off beat' is the strum you play on each count of '&'.

You will recognise the rhythm. It is used all the time in reggae music.

STRAIGHT EIGHTS

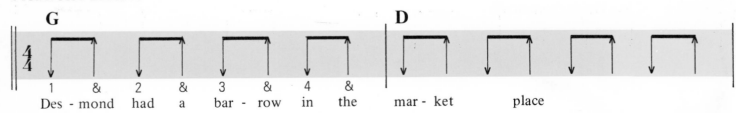

G   D

1   &   2   &   3   &   4   &
Des - mond   had   a   bar - row   in   the   mar - ket   place

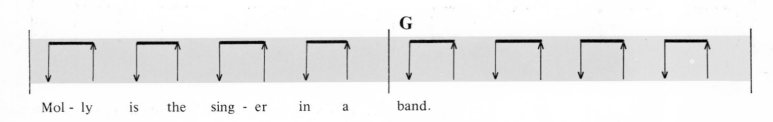

G

Mol - ly   is   the   sing - er   in   a   band.

Ob-La-Di, Ob-La-Da Continued

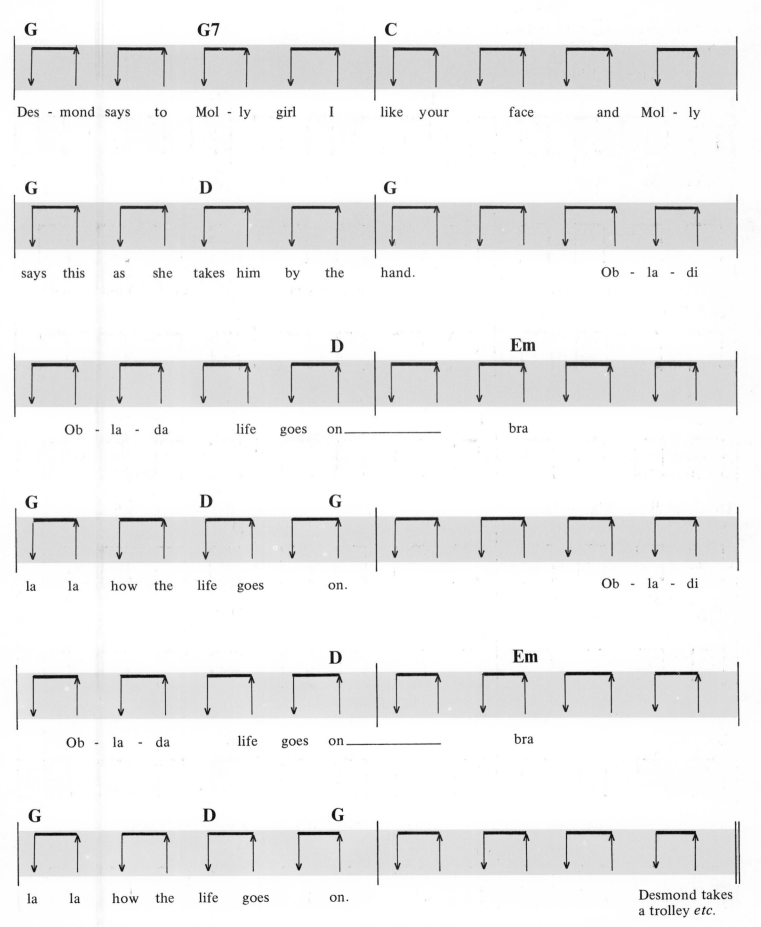

G		G7		C			
Des-	mond says	to	Mol - ly	girl	I	like your	face and Mol - ly

G		D		G			
says	this	as	she takes	him	by the	hand.	Ob - la - di

		D		Em			
Ob -	la - da		life goes	on_____		bra	

G		D		G			
la	la	how	the	life goes	on.	Ob - la - di	

		D		Em			
Ob -	la - da		life goes	on_____		bra	

G		D		G			
la	la	how	the	life goes	on.	Desmond takes a trolley *etc*.	

N.B. The full lyric for each song can be found at the back of the book.

Karma Chameleon

Words & Music: O'Dowd, Moss, Hay, Craig and Pickett

The strum pattern is familiar and you know all the
chords so enjoy yourself with this famous song.

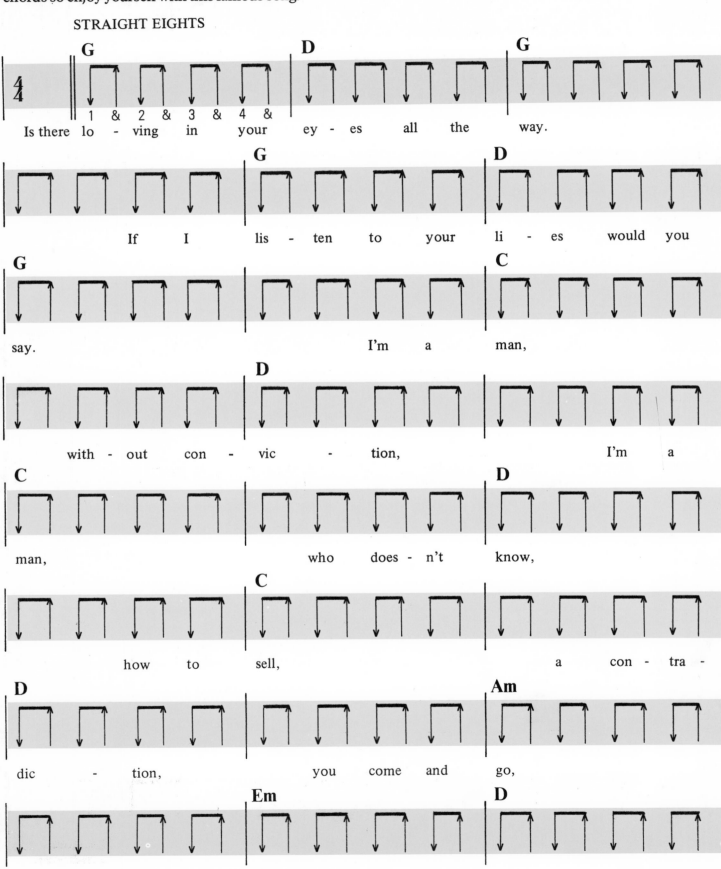

Karma Chameleon Continued

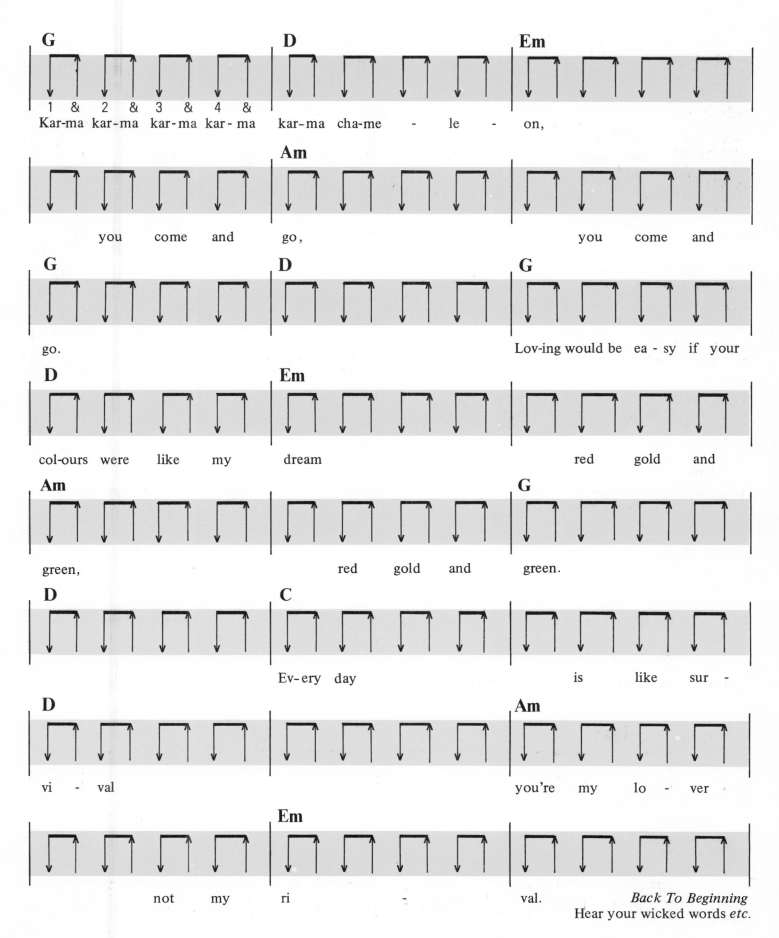

N.B. The full lyric for each song can be found at the back of the book.

Livin' On A Prayer

Words & Music: John Bon Jovi, Richie Sambora & Desmond Child

The E minor 7 Chord

The Em7 Chord

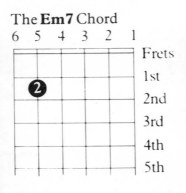

This massive hit by Bon Jovi introduces a subtle variation on the Em chord you have already learnt. Play the Em chord - which should be familiar by now - and simply remove your third finger. You should find you are making the shape shown above. Notice the subtle difference between Em and Em7.

Later you will learn how to turn all your minors into minor sevenths, but for now Em7 is all you need.

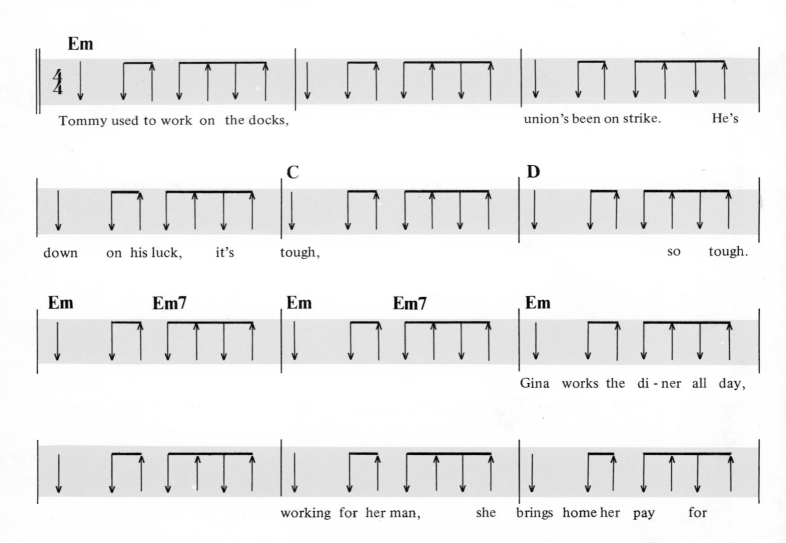

Em

Tommy used to work on the docks, union's been on strike. He's

down on his luck, it's C tough, D so tough.

Em Em7 Em Em7 Em

Gina works the di-ner all day,

working for her man, she brings home her pay for

28

Livin' On A Prayer Continued

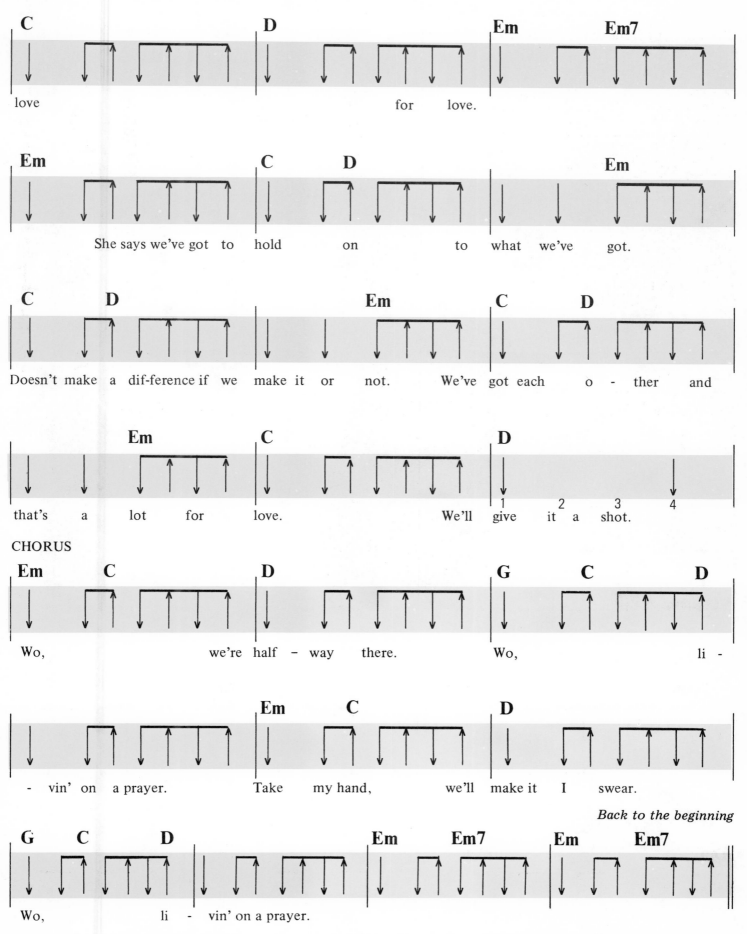

N.B. The full lyric for each song can be found at the back of the book.

My Own Way
Words & Music: Duran Duran

This big hit by Duran Duran doesn't introduce anything new. Apart from being a great song it uses seven chords you already know and makes a great practice piece. Remember, one of the secrets of being a good guitar player is being able to change smoothly from one chord to another and here's a great chance to practise this. Watch the rhythm pattern in the last eight bars. The rest sign 𝄾 which was introduced in 'That'll Be The Day' means you don't play anything on that beat.

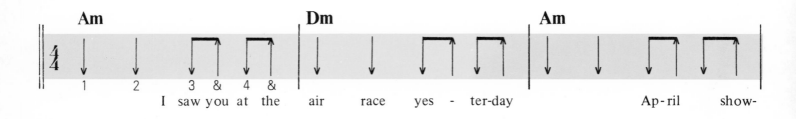

Am	Dm	Am

1   2   3 & 4 &   I saw you at the   air   race   yes - ter-day   Ap - ril   show-

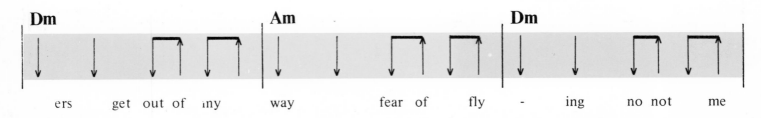

Dm	Am	Dm

ers   get out of my   way   fear of   fly -   ing   no not   me

My Own Way   Continued

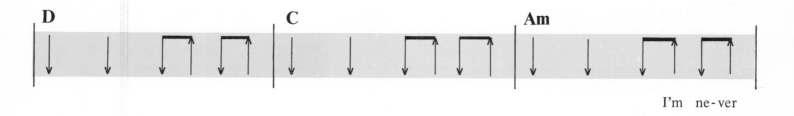

D   **C**   **Am**

I'm ne-ver

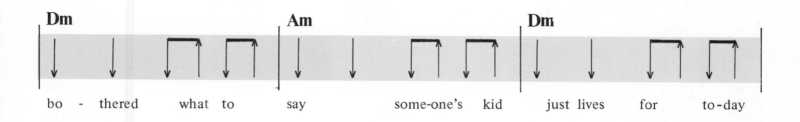

Dm   **Am**   **Dm**

bo - thered   what to   say   some-one's kid   just lives   for   to-day

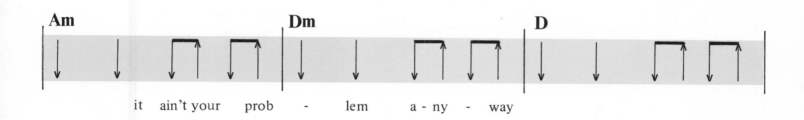

Am   **Dm**   **D**

it   ain't your   prob   -   lem   a - ny - way

CHORUS

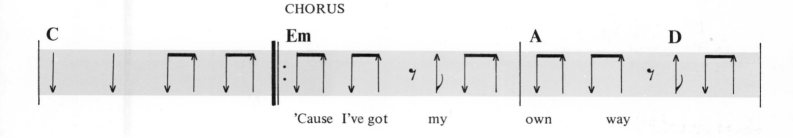

C   **Em**   **A**   **D**

'Cause I've got   my   own   way

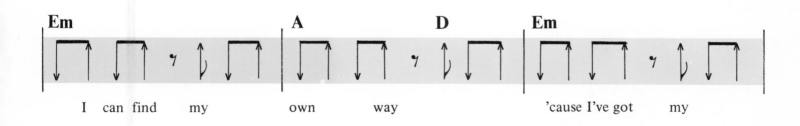

Em   **A**   **D**   **Em**

I   can find   my   own   way   'cause I've got   my

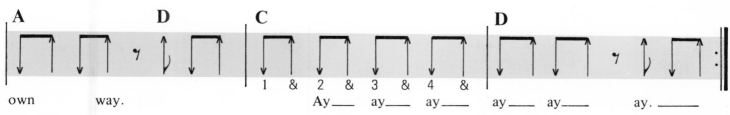

A   **D**   **C**   **D**

own   way.   1 & 2 & 3 & 4 &   Ay___ ay___ ay___   ay ___ ay___   ay. ____

Repeat
Last 8 Bars.

N.B. The full lyric for each song can be found at the back of the book.

Sailing
Words & Music: Gavin Sutherland

For Rod Stewart's big hit 'Sailing', a style of playing is introduced which allows you to add a bass line to your strumming. The letters you see incorporated with the strum marks refer to single notes and you are going to learn where to find them on the guitar. The G is played with the finger stopping the 3rd fret on the 6th string (you'll find your finger is already there to play the G chord), the F♯ is 6th string 2nd fret, the E is the open 6th string, A is open A and the C is found 3rd fret 5th string.

Simply play the note where shown and strum the appropriate chord. You'll find you're playing a very nice bass line to go with this great hit.

Sailing Continued

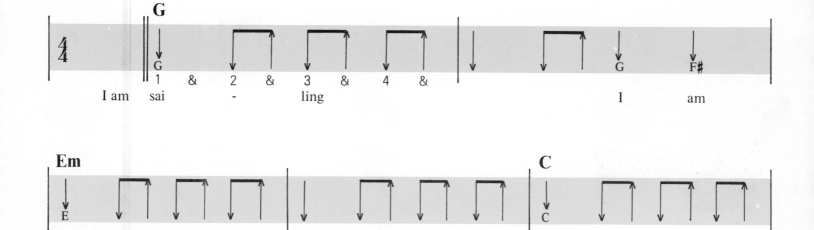

I am   sai   -   ling   I   am

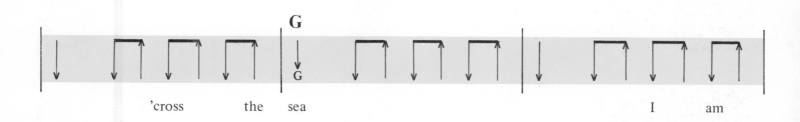

sai   -   ling   home   a   -   gain

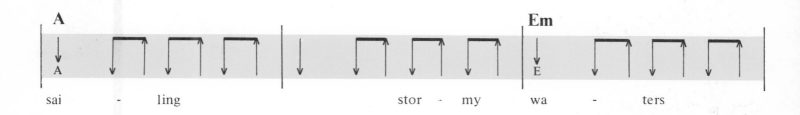

'cross   the   sea   I   am

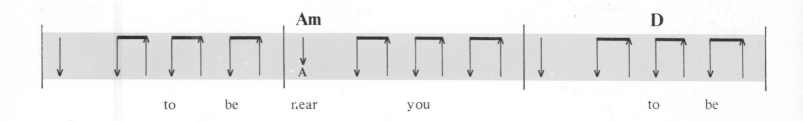

sai   -   ling   stor   -   my   wa   -   ters

to   be   near   you   to   be

free.   I   am

Back To Beginning

N.B. The full lyric for each song can be found at the back of the book.

One More Night
Words & Music: Phil Collins

The B minor Chord

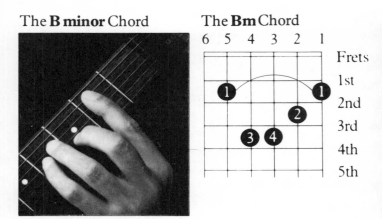

The Bm Chord

This fantastic hit by Phil Collins introduces a very important chord shape. All the chords you have previously learnt have used some open strings, whereas with this all the strings you strum are being 'stopped' with your fingers. This means that you can move the shape up and down the neck to make different chords, in this case minors. For instance, if you move your hand up one fret from the position shown, you will be playing **Cm**, up two frets and you're playing **C♯m**. We won't dwell on this for now, but isn't it great to know that in one go you've learnt possibly 10 minor chords?

For the purpose of this book, the timing of the middle section has been very slightly altered to make it easier to play.

STRAIGHT EIGHTS

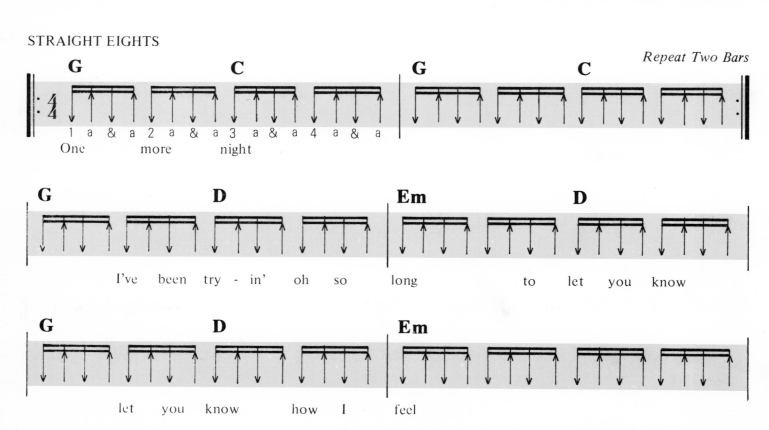

Repeat Two Bars

| G | C | G | C |

1 a & a 2 a & a 3 a & a 4 a & a

One more night

| G | D | Em | D |

I've been try - in' oh so long to let you know

| G | D | Em |

let you know how I feel

One More Night Continued

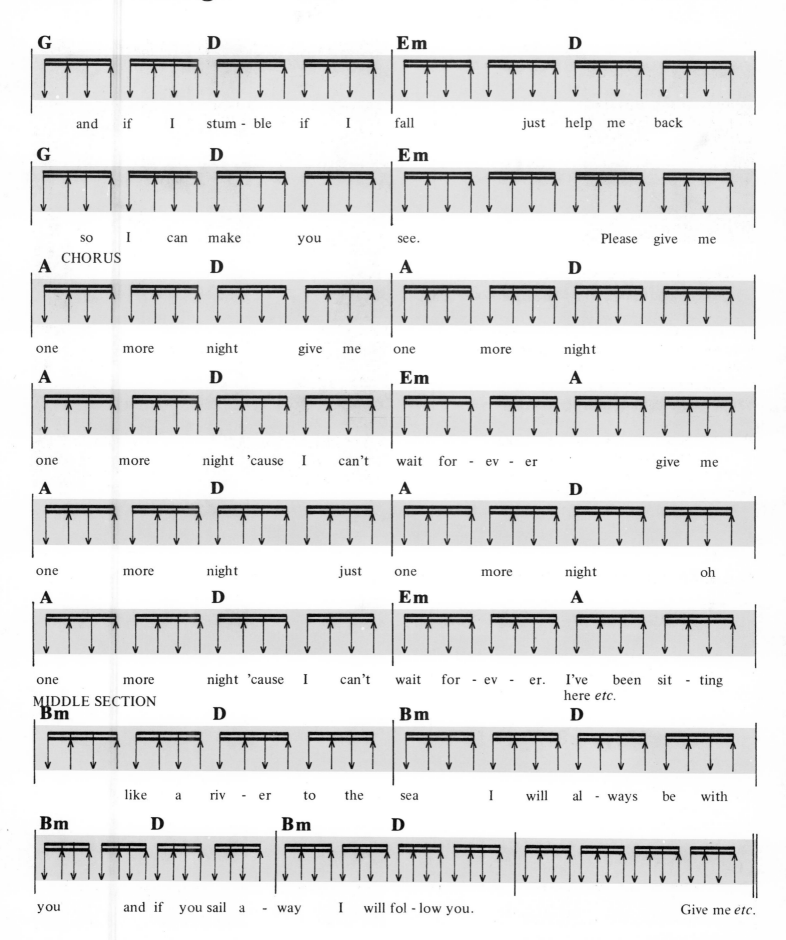

G   D   Em   D

and if I stum - ble if I fall just help me back

G   D   Em

so I can make you see. Please give me

CHORUS

A   D   A   D

one more night give me one more night

A   D   Em   A

one more night 'cause I can't wait for - ev - er give me

A   D   A   D

one more night just one more night oh

A   D   Em   A

one more night 'cause I can't wait for - ev - er. I've been sit - ting here *etc.*

MIDDLE SECTION

Bm   D   Bm   D

like a riv - er to the sea I will al - ways be with

Bm   D   Bm   D

you and if you sail a - way I will fol - low you. Give me *etc.*

Words & Music: Phil Collins

N.B. The full lyric for each song can be found at the back of the book.

Dance Away The Heartaches

Words & Music: Bryan Ferry

The **F♯ minor** Chord

The **F♯m** Chord

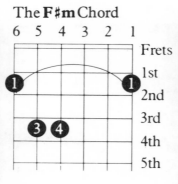

Well, you need only one more chord to play along with Bryan Ferry and 'Dance Away The Heartaches'. This shape is another moveable one, like the **Bm** in the previous piece. In the position shown above it is **F♯ minor.** Move it up one fret and it becomes **G minor,** down a fret it becomes **F minor.**

Try putting your first finger across the six strings and getting each note to sound clearly before adding your third and fourth fingers. You'll find it's easier that way.

Well folks, that's it. Keep practising. You are now ready for Book 2. There's lots more exciting things to come.

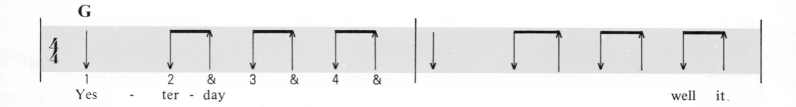

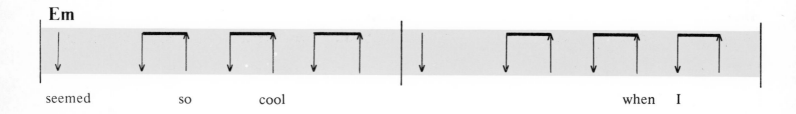

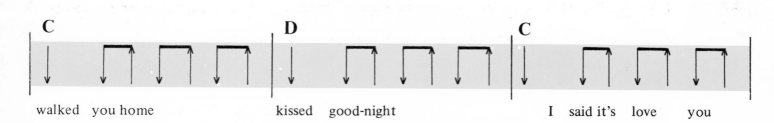

Dance Away The Heartaches Continued

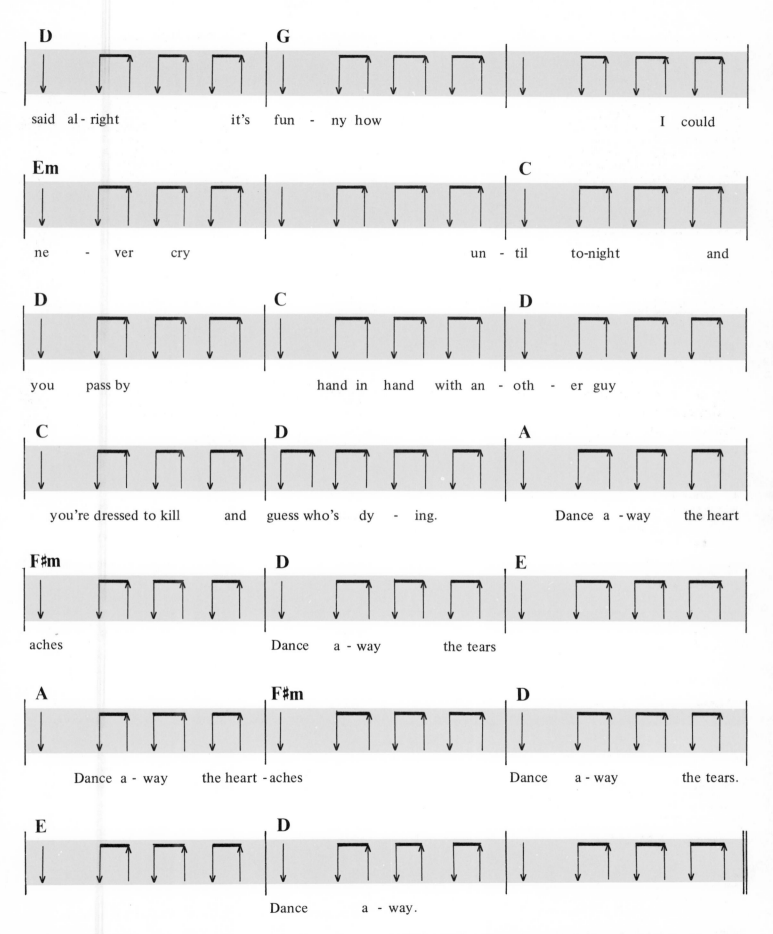

D said al - right it's fun - ny how I could

Em ne - ver cry **C** un - til to-night and

D you pass by **C** hand in hand with an - oth - er guy **D**

C you're dressed to kill and **D** guess who's dy - ing. **A** Dance a - way the heart

F#m aches **D** Dance a - way the tears **E**

A Dance a - way the heart - aches **F#m** **D** Dance a - way the tears.

E Dance a - way. **D**

Words & Music: Bryan Ferry

N.B. The full lyric for each song can be found at the back of the book.

Mull Of Kintyre

Mull of Kintyre,
Oh mist rolling in from the sea,
My desire is always to be here,
Oh Mull of Kintyre.

Far have I travelled and much have I seen,
Dark distant mountains with valleys of green,
Past painted deserts, the sunset's on fire,
As he carries me home to the Mull of Kintyre.

Mull of Kintyre,
Oh mist rolling in from the sea,
My desire is always to be here,
Oh Mull of Kintyre.

Smiles in the sunshine and tears in the rain,
Still take me back where my mem'ries remain.
Flickering embers grow higher and high'r
As they carry me back to the Mull of Kintyre.

Mull of Kintyre,
Oh mist rolling in from the sea,
My desire is always to be here,
Oh Mull of Kintyre.

Sweep through the heather like deer in the glen,
Carry me back to the days I knew then.
Nights when we sang like a heavenly choir
Of the life and the times of the Mull of Kintyre.

Mull of Kintyre.
Mull of Kintyre.

Tom Hark

Does anybody know how long to World War III?
I want to know I've got to book my holiday.
They want me in the army, but I just can't go,
I'm far too busy list'ning to the radio.
Chorus:
The whole thing's daft, I don't know why,
You'll have to laugh or else you'll cry.
You'll have to live or else you'll die
You'll have to laugh or else you'll cry.

My friends say that we're heading for a grotty time.
It's just a load of slapstick in a pantomime.
We're heading for a disaster, well, I just don't care.
Shut your eyes and count to ten, you won't be there.

Chorus.

Summertime Blues

Well I'm a-gonna raise a fuss, I'm a-gonna raise a holler,
About a workin' all summer just to try to earn a dollar,
Ev'ry time I call my Baby, try to get a date,
My boss says, "No dice, Son, you gotta work late",
Sometimes I wonder what I'm a-gonna do,
But there ain't no cure for the Summertime Blues.

A well my Mom 'n' Papa told me, "Son, you gotta make
    some money,
If you want-ta use the car to go a ridin' next Sunday",
Well, I didn't go to work, told the boss I was sick,
"Now you can't use the car 'cause you didn't work a lick."
Sometimes I wonder what I'm a-gonna do,
But there ain't no cure for the Summertime Blues.

I'm gonna take two weeks gonna have a fine vacation,
I'm gonna take my problem to the United Nations!
Well, I called my Congressman and he said (quote)
"I'd like to help you, Son, but you're too young to vote."
Sometimes I wonder what I'm a-gonna do.
But there ain't no cure for the Summertime Blues.

Hello, I Love You

Hello, I love you,
Won't you tell me your name?
Hello, I love you,
Let me jump in your game.
Hello, I love you,
Won't you tell me your name?
Hello, I love you,
Let me jump in your game.

She's walkin' down the street,
Blind to ev'ry eye she meets,
Do you think you'll be the guy
To make the queen of the angels sigh?

Hello, I love you,
Won't you tell me your name?
Hello, I love you,
Let me jump in your game.
Hello, I love you,
Won't you tell me your name?
Hello, I love you,
Let me jump in your game.

She holds her head so high,
Like a statue in the sky.
Her arms are wicked and her legs are long,
When she moves, my brain screams out this song.

Sidewalk crouches at her feet
Like a dog that begs for something sweet.
Do you hope to make her see, you fool?
Do you hope to pluck this dusky jewel?

Hello, Hello, Hello, Hello.

Get Off Of My Cloud

I live in an apartment on the ninety-ninth floor of my
    block,
And I sit at home lookin' out the window imagining the
    world has stopped
Then in flies a guy that's all dressed up like a Union
    Jack,
He says I've won five pounds if I have his kind of
    detergent pack.
Chorus:
I said Hey (Hey) you (You) Get off of my cloud!
Hey (Hey) you (You) Get off of my cloud!
Hey (Hey) you (You) Get off of my cloud!
Don't hang around, 'cause two's a crowd on my cloud
    baby.

The telephone is ringin' I say "Hi it's me Who's there on
    the line?"
A voice says, "Hi hullo. How are you?" Well I guess I'm
    doing fine
He says, "It's three a.m. and there's too much noise
Don't you people ever want to go to bed?
Just 'cause you feel so good, do you have to drive me out
    of my head?

Chorus.

I was sick and tired, fed up with this and decided to take
    a drive down town.
It was so very quiet and peaceful. There was nobody, not
    a soul around.
I laid myself out I was so tired and I started to dream.
In the mornin' the parkin' tickets were just like flags
    stuck on my windscreen.

Chorus.

That'll Be The Day

Well, you give me all your lovin' and your turtle dovin',
All your hugs and kisses and your money too;
Well, you know you love me, baby,
Until you tell me, maybe, that some day, well, I'll be
    through!
Chorus:
Well, that'll be the day, when you say goodbye,
Yes, that'll be the day, when you make me cry,
You say you're gonna leave, you know it's a lie,
'Cause that'll be the day when I die.

When Cupid shot his dart, he shot it at your heart,
So if we ever part and I leave you,
You say you told me and you told me boldly,
That some day, well, I'll be through.

Chorus.

Black Magic Woman

Got a black magic woman.
Got a black magic woman,
I've got a black magic woman.
Got me so blind I can't see that she's a black magic
    woman,
She's try'n to make a devil out of me.

Turn your back on me baby,
Turn your back on me baby,
Yes don't turn your back on me baby.
Stop messin' round with your tricks,
Don't turn your back on me, baby, you just might pick up
    my magic sticks.

Got your spell on me baby,
Got your spell on me baby,
Yes you got your spell on me baby, turning my heart into
    stone.
I need you so bad, magic woman, I can't leave you alone.

Stand By Me

When the night has come and the land is dark,
And the moon is the only light we'll see
No I won't be afraid, no I won't be afraid
Just as long as you stand, stand by me.

So, darling, darling stand by me.
Oh, oh, stand by me, oh, stand, stand by me, stand by me.

If the sea that we look upon should tumble and fall,
Or the mountain should crumble in the sea,
I won't cry, I won't cry, no I won't shed a tear
Just as long as you stand, stand by me.

So darling, darling stand by me.
Oh, stand by me, oh, stand, stand by me, stand by me.

Paint It Black

I see a red door and I want it painted black,
No colours any more I want them to turn black,
I see the girls walk by dressed in their summer clothes.
I have to turn my head until my darkness goes.

I see a line of cars and they're all painted black,
With flowers and my love both never to come back,
I see people turn their heads and quickly look away,
Like a new born baby it just happens ev'ry day.

I look inside myself and see my heart is black,
I see my red door and I want it painted black,
Maybe then I'll fade away and not have to face the facts,
It's not easy facing up when your whole world is black.

No more will my green sea go turn a deeper blue,
I could not foresee this thing happening to you,
If I look hard enough into the setting sun,
My love will laugh with me before the morning comes.

I see a red door and I want it painted black,
No colours any more I want them to turn black,
I see the girls walk by dressed in their summer clothes,
I have to turn my head until my darkness goes.

Ob-La-Di Ob-La-Da

Desmond had a barrow in the market place,
Molly is the singer in a band.
Desmond says to Molly, girl I like your face
And Molly says this as she takes him by the hand.
Ob-la-di, ob-la-da, life goes on bra.
La la how the life goes on.
Ob-la-di, ob-la-da, life goes on bra.
La la how the life goes on.

Desmond takes a trolley to the jeweller's store,
Buys a twenty carat golden ring,
Takes it back to Molly, waiting at the door
And as he gives it to her she begins to sing.
Ob-la-di, ob-la-da, life goes on bra.
La la how the life goes on.
Ob-la-di, ob-la-da, life goes on bra.
La la how the life goes on.

In a couple of years they have built a home sweet home
With a couple of kids running in the yard of Desmond
    and Molly Jones.

Happy ever after in the market place,
Desmond lets the children lend a hand.
Molly stays at home and does her pretty face
And in the evening she still sings it with the band.
Ob-la-di, ob-la-da, life goes on bra.
La la how the life goes on.
Ob-la-di, ob-la-da, life goes on bra.
La la how the life goes on.

Karma Chameleon

Is there loving in your eyes all the way?
If I listen to your lies would you say
I'm a man, without conviction?
I'm a man who doesn't know
How to sell a contradiction,
You come and go you come and go.

Karma karma karma karma karma chameleon
You come and go you come and go
Loving would be easy if your colours were like my dream
Red gold and green, red gold and green.

Hear your wicked words every day
And you used to be so sweet. I heard you say
That my love was an addiction.
When we cling our love is strong,
When you go you're gone forever,
You string along you string along.

Karma karma karma karma karma chameleon
You come and go you come and go
Loving would be easy if your colours were like my dream
Red gold and green, red gold and green.

Every day is like survival
You're my lover not my rival.

Dancing In The Dark

I get up in the evening,
And I ain't got nothin' to say.
I come home in the morning,
I go to bed feeling the same way.
I ain't nothin' but tired.
Man I'm just tired and bored with myself.
Hey there baby, I could use just a little help.
Chorus:
You can't start a fire,
You can't start a fire without a spark.
This gun's for hire
Even if we're just dancing in the dark.

Message keeps getting clearer,
Radio's on and I'm moving 'round the place.
I check my look in the mirror;
I wanna change my clothes, my hair, my face.
Man, I ain't getting nowhere
Just living in a dump like this.
There's something happening somewhere;
Baby I just know there is.

Chorus.

Stay on the streets of this town
And they'll be carving you up all right.
They say you got to stay hungry;
Hey baby I'm just about starving tonight.
I'm dying for some action;
I'm sick of sitting 'round here trying to write this book.
I need a love reaction;
Come on now baby gimme just one look.

Chorus.

You can't start a fire,
Sitting 'round crying over a broken heart.
This gun's for hire
Even if we're just dancing in the dark.

You sit around getting older;
There's a joke here somewhere, and it's on me.
I'll shake this world off my shoulders,
Come on baby, the laugh's on me.

You can't start a fire
Worrying about your little world falling apart
This gun's for hire
Even if we're just dancing in the dark.
Even if we're just dancing in the dark.

My Own Way

I saw you at the air race yesterday
April showers get out of my way.
Fear of flying? No not me.
I'm never bothered what to say.
Someone's kid just lives for today.
It ain't your problem anyway.
Chorus:
'Cause I've got my own way.
I can find my own way.
'Cause I've got my own way,
Ay ay ay ay ay ay
'Cause I've got my own way.
I can find my own way
Ay ay ay ay ay
Number one.

Public figure what a pain
Just puts another rattle in your brain.
Take another green but it's not the same.
So now you're on the sand lane every day.
Dancing with the bulls in any old way.
Running like a fox to keep up with me.

Chorus.

I'm on forty-five, forty-five,
Three six and Broadway,
Broadway, now Broadway,
Now Broadway, now Broadway.

Sailing

I am sailing, I am sailing,
Home again 'cross the sea.
I am sailing stormy waters,
To be near you to be free.

I am flying, I am flying,
Like a bird 'cross the sky.
I am flying passing high clouds,
To be with you to be free.

Can you hear me, can you hear me,
Thro' the dark night far away.
I am dying forever trying,
To be with you who can say.

Can you hear me, can you hear me,
Thro' the dark night far away.
I am dying, forever trying,
To be with you who can say.

We are sailing, we are sailing,
Home again 'cross the sea.
We are sailing, stormy waters,
To be near you to be free.

Oh Lord to be near you
To be free.
Oh Lord to be near you
To be free.

One More Night

One more night,
One more night.

I've been trying oh so long to let you know,
Let you know how I feel.
And if I stumble if I fall,
Just help me back so I can make you see.
Chorus:
Please give me one more night.
Give me one more night.
One more night, 'cause I can't wait forever.
Give me one more night,
Just one more night.
Oh, one more night, 'cause I can't wait forever.

I've been sitting here so long, wasting time,
Just staring at the phone.
And I was wond'ring should I call you,
Then I thought maybe you're not alone.

Chorus.

I know there'll never be a time you'll ever feel the same.
And I know it's only words.
But if you change your mind,
You know that I'll be here, and maybe we both can learn.

Chorus.

Give me one more night.
Give me just one more night.
One more night 'cause I can't wait forever.

Like a river to the sea,
I will always be with you.
And if you sail away,
I will follow you.

Give me one more night,
Give me just one more night,
Oh, one more night, 'cause I can't wait forever.

Give me just a one more night.
Give me just a one more night,
One more night. 'Cause I can't wait forever.

Give me just a one more night.
Give me just a one more night,
One more night. 'Cause I can't wait forever.

Dance Away The Heartaches

Yesterday, well it seemed so cool,
When I walked you home kissed goodnight,
I said "It's love", you said "Alright".
It's funny how I could never cry
Until tonight and you pass by,
Hand in hand with another guy,
You're dressed to kill and guess who's dying?
Chorus:

Dance away the heartaches, dance away the tears.
Dance away the heartaches , dance away the tears
Dance away.

Loneliness is a crowded room
Full of open hearts, turned to stone,
All together, all alone.
All at once my whole world had changed,
Now I'm in the dark, off the wall,
Let the strobe light up them all,
I close my eyes and dance till dawn.
Chorus:
Now I know I must walk the line,
Until I find an open door,
Off the street on to the floor.
There was I many times a fool,
I hope and pray but not too much,
Out of reach is out of touch,
All the way is far enough.

Chorus.
Dance away.
Dance away.
Dance away.
Dance away the heartaches, dance away the tears.
Dance away the heartaches, dance away the tears.
Dance away the heartaches, dance away the tears.
Dance away the heartaches, dance away the tears.

The Complete Rock & Pop Guitar Player

by Mick Barker, Rick Cardinali, Roger Day.

Book 2

Songs included in this book

Reading Music Made Easy

The music we play is written on five equally spaced lines called a stave (staff).

Staves are divided into bars (or measures) by the use of a vertical line.

Each *bar* has a fixed number of *beats* in it. A *beat* is the natural tapping rhythm of a song. Most songs have four *beats* in each *bar*, and we can tap our feet or count along with these songs.

Occasionally, there are three *beats* in each *bar*, and we count like this:

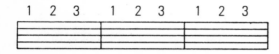

How do we know the number of *beats* in a bar of music simply by looking at it?

At the beginning of every piece of music there is a time signature which gives us this information. It consists of two numbers, one above the other. The top number tells us how many beats there are in each bar, the lower number tells us the value of these beats as expressed in the musical notation which we use (we shall come to notes shortly).

In simple music which is used in these books we see the three most common time signatures

4

4 is often shown as **C**, or Common Time.

Once given, the *time signature* is not repeated, unless the *beat* changes within a song. This happens only occasionally in rock music.

The symbol we see at the beginning of each *stave* is called the *treble clef*.

There are other clefs, but the *treble clef* is used for all the songs in this book. What is a clef? Well, a clef fixes the *pitch* of a given note within a *stave*. The *treble clef* is used here because it fixes the most suitable *pitch* for singing the songs in these books.

In music there are various standard markings which can be used to abbreviate the layout. When we come to this sign

it tells us to go back to where this sign appears

(or, sometimes, when this does not appear, we return to the beginning) and repeat the section.

Sometimes we repeat the whole section, but the ending of the 'second time through' can be different from the first time. Thus we have what are called 1st and 2nd time bars (or a 3rd and 4th for that matter). Here is an example:

The first time through, we play bars 1 & 2. The second time we play bars 1 & 3.

We often see the letters D.C. & D.S. at the end of a stave line. D.C. (from the Italian *da capo*) tells us to return to the beginning ('top'). D.S. *(dal segno)* means return to the sign, ％. After these letters we see the words *al coda* (to the *coda*) or *al fine* (to the finish).

The *coda* is the end section of a song, usually short. Here is an example:

Here we play bars 1 – 3. We are then directed back to bar 2, and continue to bar 3, when the sign ⊕ above the bar line tells us to jump to the *coda* at bar 4.

Here is another example:

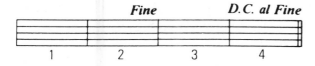

Play bars 1 – 4. Then return to bar 1, and continue to bar 2, where the word *Fine* (or end) tells us to stop. Sometimes coupled with the word *Fine* we see the sign ⌢ over a chord or note. This means you pause on the beat marked, letting the final chord ring. This is a very common ending.

✗ means that you should repeat the preceding bar

is played.

means that you should repeat the preceding two bars

NOTES – VALUES – TIES

Now we come to *notes* and their time values. The *notes* tell the player exactly *what to play, how to play it*, and *when to play it*.

Semibreve, (or whole note)

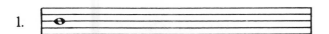

Minims, (or half notes)

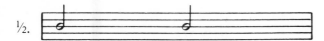

Crotchets, (or quarter notes)

Quavers, (or eighth notes)

Semiquavers, (or sixteenth notes)

The notes in each stave of the chart all add up to 4 beats, the beat being a crotchet.

So in a piece of music in $\frac{4}{4}$ time we count 4 beats to the bar, each beat being one crotchet.

A bar in $\frac{2}{4}$ time will contain two crotchet beats to the bar.

The same principle applies to 3/4 time:

Here we see a minim with a *dot* after it. The *dot* increases by a half the time value of any note after which it is placed.

Many guitar accompaniments consist of strumming 8 quavers to each bar of 4/4 time. We still count 4 crotchets, but to maintain an easy rhythm we count 1 & 2 & 3 & 4 &, each syllable being one quaver value (1/8)

Sometimes we see dotted quavers and semiquavers joined together. Again we count four, but the rhythm does not flow smoothly as with 8 quavers to the bar, and we count like this:

1 & a 2 & a 3 & a 4 & a

Just as notes tell us when to play, we have *rests* which tell us when *not* to play. There is a rest which corresponds in value to each type of note.

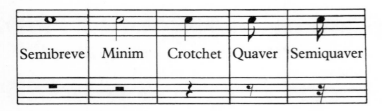

Semibreve	Minim	Crotchet	Quaver	Semiquaver

Similarly, dotted rests have the same time values as dotted notes.

A whole bar's rest is generally shown by a semibreve rest, whether or not the music is in 4/4 time.

Here is the scale of C major
A tone (T) is made up of 2 semitones (S/T) and semitones correspond to the frets on your guitar.
i.e. C to D is a tone or two frets
E to F is a semitone or one fret.

C D E F G A B C

This is an *octave* and can be repeated up or down the stave. The first C is below the stave and we see that a *ledger line* runs through the note. This is an extension of the stave to accommodate the note. Here are more examples:

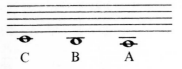

C B A

At the beginning of each stave line, we see, after the treble clef, the *key signature* of the music. This consists of sharps or flats or, in the case of C major or A minor none at all, and indicates that all notes against which they are set should be raised or lowered by a semitone.

Here, *all* Fs are to be raised by a semitone in all *octaves*.

Here, *all* Bs and Es are to be lowered by a semitone in all octaves.

It is necessary sometimes to insert sharps or flats that do not occur in the *key signatures*, they are called accidentals. In this case we put the sign before the individual note, and its effect lasts for *one bar only*. The natural sign ♮ is also used to countermand a sharp or flat given in the key signature. Again its effect is for one bar only:

or or

Finally, we come to the curved line, which, in its various functions, will occur in these books.

It has the effect of joining together two notes.

When you see two notes of the same pitch tied together you simply play the first one and let it ring on through the note to which it is tied.

44

Another line often seen on vocal music is the syllable line:

ba - by   come back and stay

Here the line groups together notes to be sung on one syllable. Where the word is of two or more syllables, they are separated by a hyphen. Monosyllabic words simply have a straight line after them for the duration of the syllable line.

These are the outlines of reading and understanding simple music.

The songs, whether rock standards or up-to-date hits, will probably be familiar to you, so that by singing what you already know and matching it with the printed music you will understand the various combinations of notes.

Tablature Explained

The tablature stave comprises six lines, each representing a string on the guitar as illustrated.

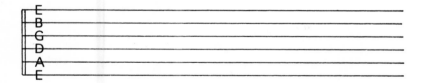

A number on any of the lines indicates, therefore, the string and fret on which a note should be played.

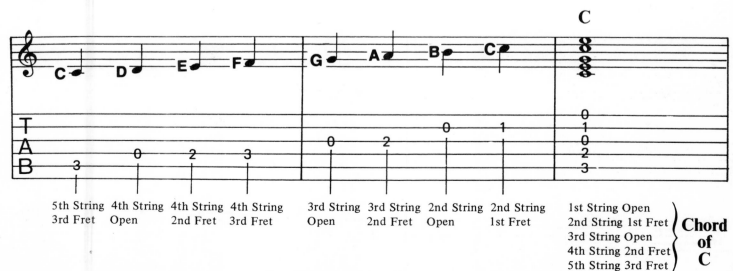

| 5th String 3rd Fret | 4th String Open | 4th String 2nd Fret | 4th String 3rd Fret | 3rd String Open | 3rd String 2nd Fret | 2nd String Open | 2nd String 1st Fret | 1st String Open
2nd String 1st Fret
3rd String Open
4th String 2nd Fret
5th String 3rd Fret } Chord of C |

Come Back And Stay

Words & Music: Jack Lee

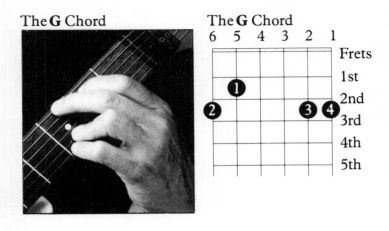

The G Chord

The first tune you're going to learn in the second book of the series is that smash hit for Paul Young 'Come Back And Stay'. You'll recognise the names of all the chords you're using from Book 1 but you will also see that there is a new version of the **G** chord to learn. It would be quite correct to play this song using the old 'G Shape' but try the new one and see how it gives the chord a completely different 'flavour'. To recap, the two are completely interchangeable and whenever you see a **G** chord symbol you can try both shapes and see which sound you prefer. It's all good practice.

The other new point to learn is how to 'damp' the strings. In bars 13 to 17 you'll see the 2nd, 3rd, and 4th beats are marked 'damped'. To do this simply rest the side of your hand lightly on the strings just before they cross the bridge and you'll find it gives a nice 'chunky' sound.

The opposite to damped is 'open', which means let the strings ring.

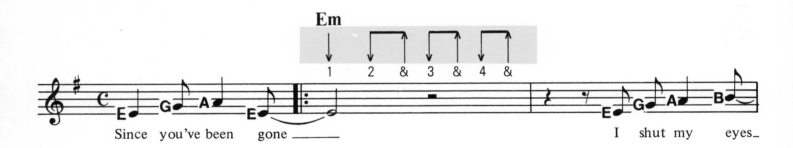

Since you've been gone _____ I shut my eyes_

_____ and I fan - ta - sise _____ that you're here with

me. Will you ev - er re - turn? _____

I won't be sat - is - fied _____ 'till you're by my side _____

Come Back And Stay Continued

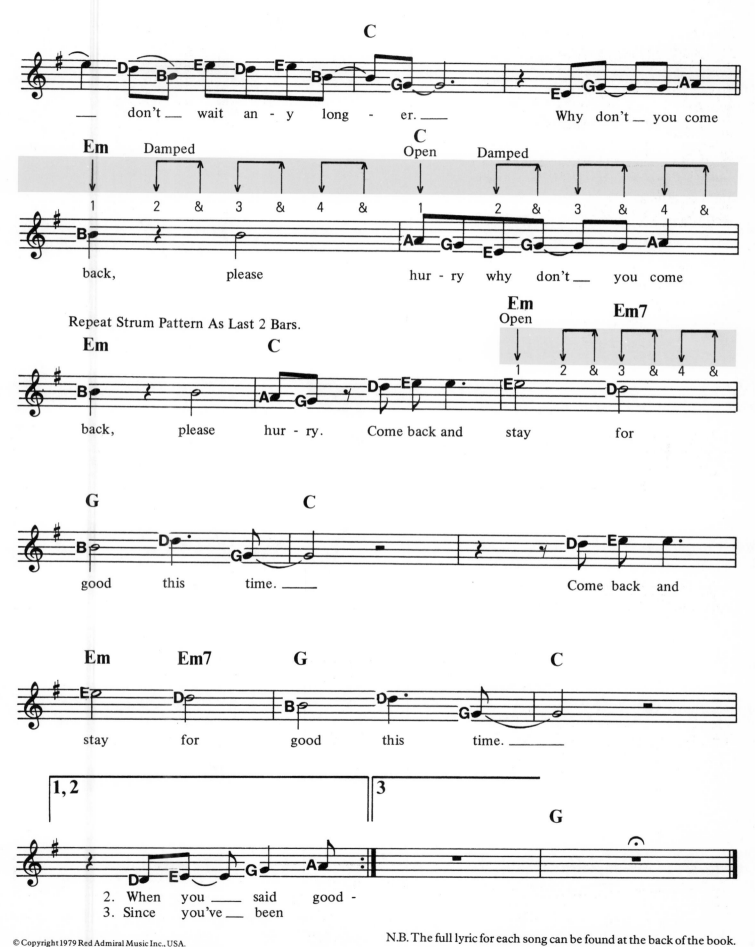

N.B. The full lyric for each song can be found at the back of the book.

Moonlight Shadow

Words & Music: Mike Oldfield

This classic from Mike Oldfield also uses easy chords from Book One. Apart from being a great little song it is a very good practice piece.

Before you start, have a quick look at the middle section ('I stay...' etc.). You'll find there's a quick change between the **D** and the **G** chords. In the same section you'll also find very effective semiquaver strums at the end of some of the bars. You'll recognise the effect immediately: it's part of every Rock 'n' Pop guitarist's repertoire.

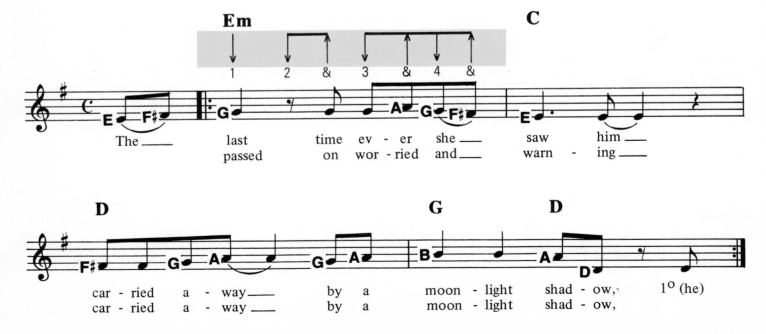

The _____ last time ev - er she _____ saw him _____
passed on wor - ried and _____ warn - ing _____

car - ried a - way _____ by a moon - light shad - ow, 1° (he)
car - ried a - way _____ by a moon - light shad - ow,

Moonlight Shadow Continued

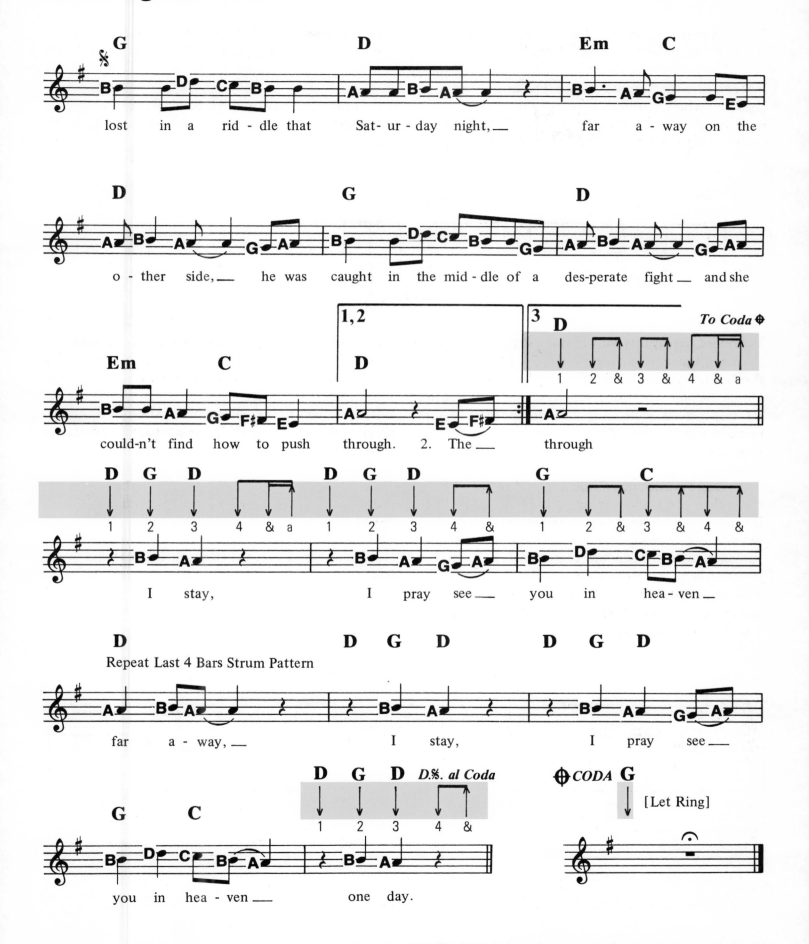

N.B. The full lyric for each song can be found at the back of the book.

49

Hey Joe   Words & Music: William M. Roberts

This next song is important because, once mastered, it will be a landmark in your progress.

There are two new points to learn. The first is the tie sign, ⌢ which you read about in the section on musical notation. As you know, it is used to tie two notes of the same pitch together so that only the first of the tied notes is played. The effect of a tie sign between two or more differently pitched notes will be dealt with in later books.

In the example below, which is in fact Bar 3 of 'Hey Joe', the tie sign is applied to strum marks with exactly the same effect.

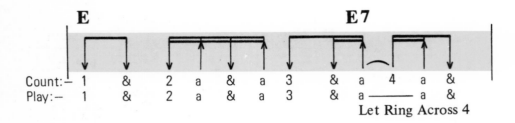

Therefore, to play this bar, you must strum all the marks as shown, but leave out the one that falls directly over the 4 (which you will notice does not have an arrow), letting the previous strum (which is a chord change to **E7**) ring instead. So, to recap, a tie sign means: play the first of the tied notes and let ring, but don't play the second note.

The second is this catchy little riff which fits perfectly under the chords, and is instantly recognisable as the famous bass riff from the Jimi Hendrix smash hit recording of this song. You have seen the tablature explanation at the beginning of this book; well, this is your first chance to use your new ability. It's easy, just remember that the tablature lines represent the 6 strings on the guitar, and let the numbers guide your fingers to the correct fret.

The timing is easy because the riff is a straight eight pattern. Practise it very slowly and evenly before attempting to play it at the correct tempo.

When you have mastered the strum pattern and vocals, try using the riff instead of the chords the second time you play each vocal line.

C   G   D   A   E
Hey Joe where ya goin' with that gun in your hand?
Strum

Hey Joe where ya goin' with that gun in your hand?
Riff------

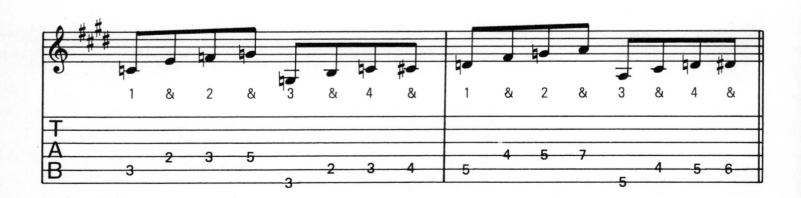

Hey Joe Continued

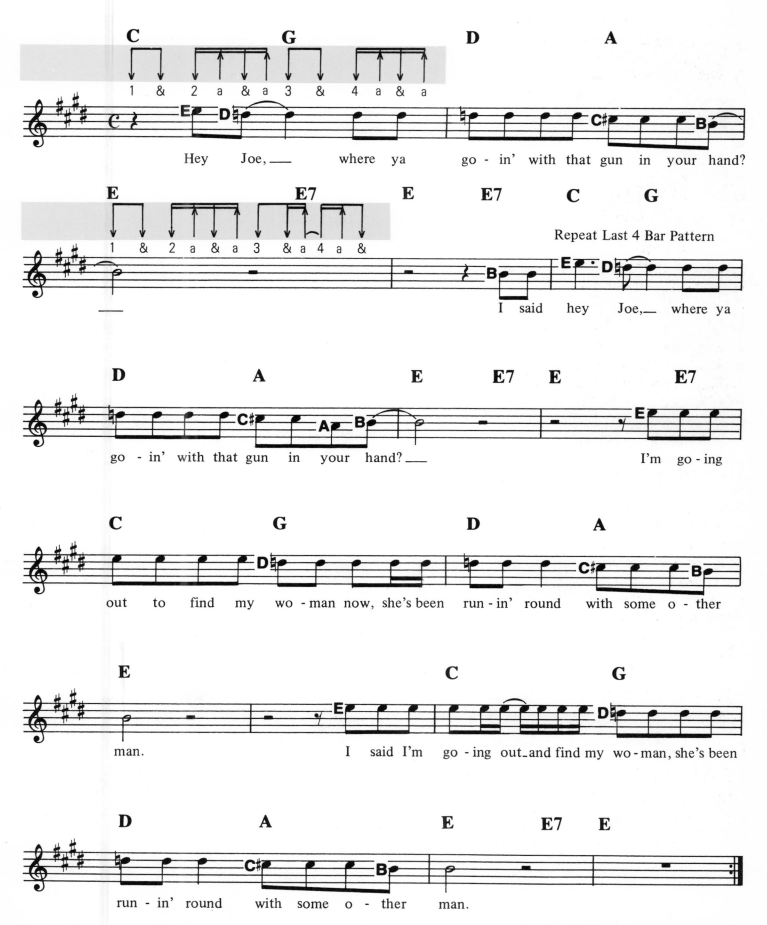

N.B. The full lyric for each song can be found at the back of the book.

Honky Tonk Women

Words & Music: Mick Jagger and Keith Richards

The **B7** Chord

The **B7** Chord

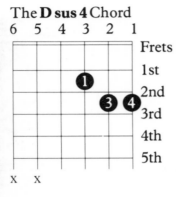

The **D Sus 4** Chord

The **D sus 4** Chord

This rhythm and blues classic by The Rolling Stones introduces your first 'sus 4' chord. Without being too technical at this stage, it is sufficient to say that a **'sus 4'** chord contains a note that is not really part of the chord.

Before you go any further, try playing the **'D sus 4'** followed by a normal **D** chord, familiar isn't it? You will find that composers nearly always follow a **'sus 4'** chord with a 'straight' version of the same chord (**D sus 4** to **D** – **A sus 4** to **A**).

The **B7** Chord is self explanatory.

To get the proper effect in bar 3, make the up strokes on the '&' of 3 and the '&' of 4 louder than the other strums. This is called accenting them and is shown in musical notation by putting a ' > ' sign over the top of the note or strum mark.

As a final note remember that

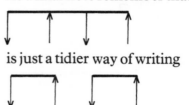

is just a tidier way of writing

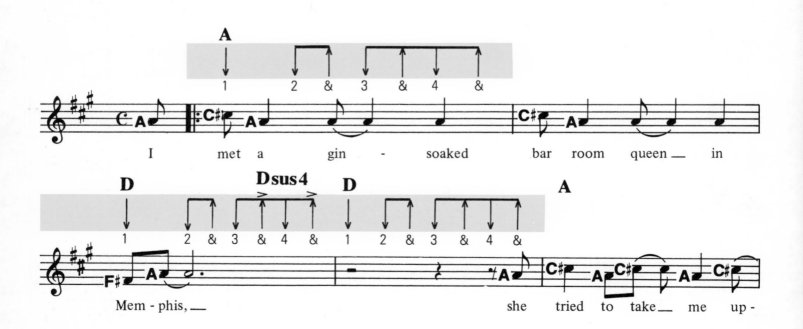

Honky Tonk Women   Continued

N.B. The full lyric for each song can be found at the back of the book.

Light My Fire
Words & Music: The Doors

The **B minor 7** Chord

The **Bm7** Chord

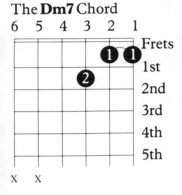

The **D minor 7** Chord

The **Dm7** Chord

This great song has been a hit for several performers. The most famous was the original version by The Doors with Jim Morrison on vocals. It introduces slightly different versions of two chords you learnt in Book One.

As always at this stage, when practising minor sevenths play a straight minor version of the chord first, followed by the minor seventh, and listen to the subtle difference in sound.

The **Dm7** is very simple and needs no explanation, but for the **Bm7** you may need to refer back to the **Bm** shape introduced in Book One.

Simply play a **Bm** and take your little finger off the third string. As long as you're careful that your barré (first finger) is pressing down cleanly across the strings you should now be playing **Bm7**. As this **Bm7** shape does not use any open strings it is 'moveable', just like the **Bm** in Book 1. These two shapes both take their name from the note you are fingering on the fifth string. That is to say if:

The tip of your 1st finger is resting on the 2nd fret of the 5th string, the chord is **B minor 7**.
The tip of your 1st finger is resting on the 3rd fret of the 5th string, the chord is **C minor 7**.
The tip of your 1st finger is resting on the 5th fret of the 5th string, the chord is **D minor 7**.

Light My Fire

Continued

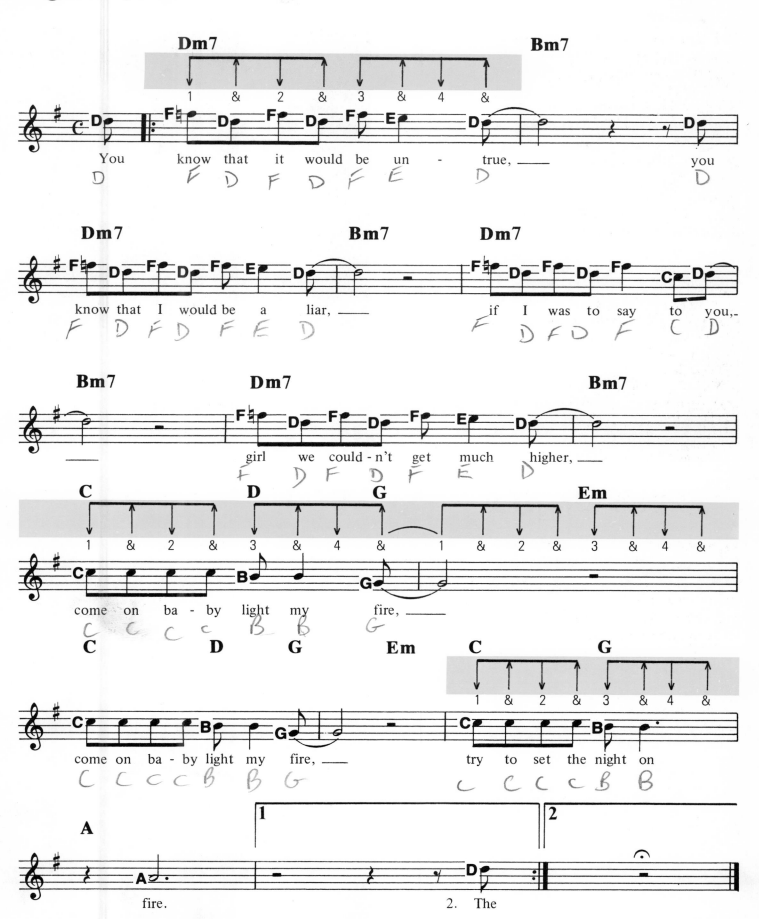

N.B. The full lyric for each song can be found at the back of the book.

So Far Away   Words & Music: Mark Knopfler

This Dire Straits hit is a song of contrasts, and since you know all the necessary chords, you should be able to concentrate your attention on a performance with 'light and shade'.

For the verse, damp the strings with the side of your right hand (as in 'Come Back & Stay' earlier in the book), then strum only the bass strings of the chord for that 'chunky' sound.

There is a 'magic moment' where in bar 8, on a count of "4 &" you see the "open" instruction. Remove your damping hand for the quick down up ' 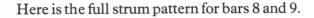 ' and change chord to G, letting the strings ring 'open' and the whole song 'open up'.

Here is the full strum pattern for bars 8 and 9.

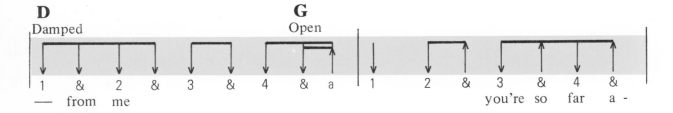

VERSE

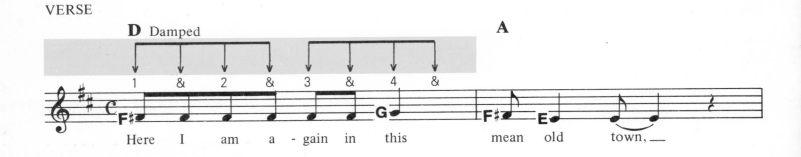

56

So Far Away   Continued

N.B. The full lyric for each song can be found at the back of the book.

I Shot The Sheriff   Words & Music: Bob Marley

INTRO RIFF

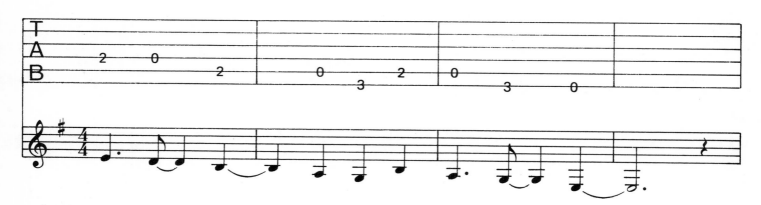

Eric Clapton had a smash hit with this Bob Marley song. The notation and tablature above give you the great little figure that goes in the last four bars before you go back to the beginning (D.C.). The strumming pattern introduces an interesting new effect, look at the first bar and I'll explain what happens.

The sign E you encountered in the first book, means you hit the bottom E string only. The strumming on beats 2 and 4 is as normal, but on beat 3 you will see

the sign ✗. In this instance it means that you hit all six strings with the side of your right hand, it should produce a percussive 'clicky' sound. This is a very effective reggae type rhythm and a little time spent on it will reproduce a really fantastic effect. Do exactly the same for the **A** minor chord playing the open A string on the first beat.

I Shot The Sheriff   Continued

N.B. The full lyric for each song can be found at the back of the book.

(This Could Be) The Last Time

Words & Music: Mick Jagger and Keith Richards

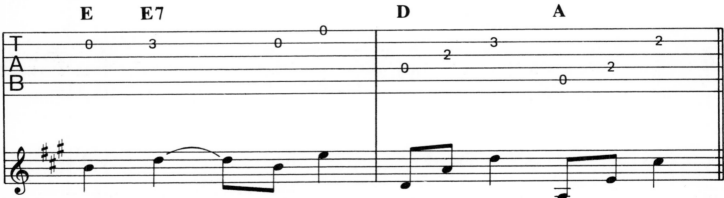

You will be familiar with the chords for this rock classic by The Rolling Stones so you will be able to concentrate on learning to play the neat little 'riff' which is written above in both notation and tablature.

Play the two bar phrase twice as an introduction. You'll also find it fits very nicely in bars 3 and 4 and 7 and 8 of the verse. Note that bar numbers should be counted from the thick Double Bar Line

If you just want to strum through these bars simply follow the chord symbols as usual.

When playing the second half of Bar 2 of the above phrase, the plectrum (or fingers of the right hand) has to 'jump' the third string. Don't worry if you can't stop it from sounding, it fits in with the chord. However, if you want it to sound exactly like the original, practise until you can play it as it's written.

(This Could Be) The Last Time   Continued

N.B. The full lyric for each song can be found at the back of the book.

Don't Pay The Ferryman

Words & Music: Chris de Burgh

The **D/F♯** Chord

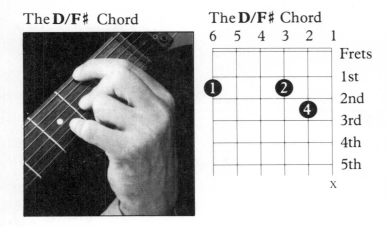

The **D/F♯** Chord

```
6  5  4  3  2  1
```
Frets
1st
2nd
3rd
4th
5th

X

This song has a chord of **D** with an F♯ in the bass which is written **D/F♯**. Try it and hear the rich resonance.

The strum pattern for this Chris De Burgh hit is familiar to you but take note that the **D** and **D/F♯** are both 'accented' (as explained in 'Honky Tonk Women'). The **D** arrives on the last 'up strum' at the end of the bar that goes '…RAIN came DOWN'. Similarly the **D/F♯** arrives on the last 'up strum' at the end of the bar that goes '…WILD dog HOWL'. This is a great effect and again is instantly recognisable from the hit record.

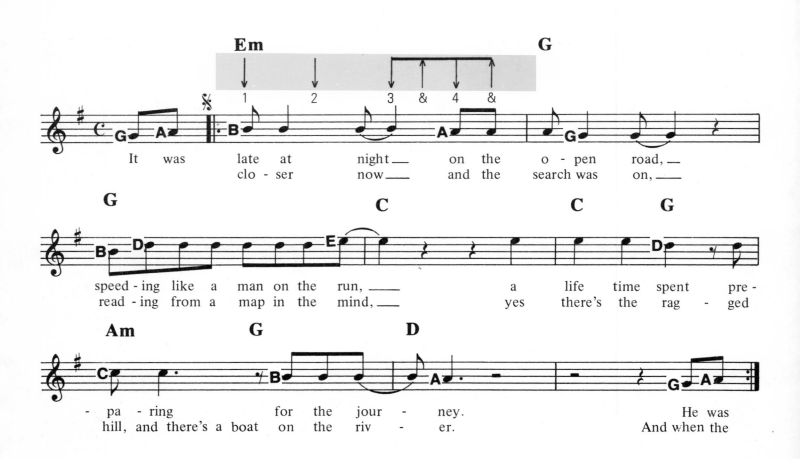

It was late at night on the o-pen road,
clo-ser now and the search was on,

speed-ing like a man on the run, a life time spent pre-
read-ing from a map in the mind, yes there's the rag-ged

-pa-ring for the jour-ney. He was
hill, and there's a boat on the riv-er. And when the

Don't Pay The Ferryman Continued

N.B. The full lyric for each song can be found at the back of the book.

My Sweet Lord Words & Music: George Harrison

The G♯ dim Chord

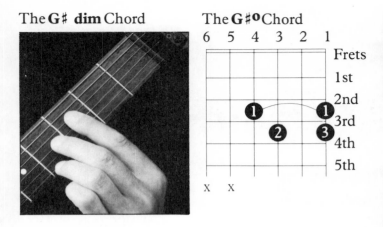

The G♯° Chord

6 5 4 3 2 1

Frets
1st
2nd
3rd
4th
5th

x x

'My Sweet Lord', written and recorded by George Harrison, was a big hit all over the world.

You only have to learn one new chord and it's one with a very interesting property. The chord is **G♯** diminished but this is usually written as **G♯ °**, the circle being a 'musical shorthand' method of writing 'diminished'. (It could also be written **G♯ dim**).

You'll see that it's a four-string chord with all the strings you are striking 'stopped' by the left hand and you know by now that means it's moveable.

At this point go back and re-read the section on **Bm7** which occurs in 'Light My Fire'. Then come back to this and you'll learn something very interesting.

Checked it out? O.K. read on.

You discovered that you can move that minor 7th shape up and down the fret board and it always takes its name from the note fingered on the fifth string. Well, the unusual fact about the diminished chord is that it can take its name from any of the notes stopped with the left hand. That means that although in this instance we have called the shape **G♯ °**, it could also be called **D°**, **B°**, or **F°**.

This will be explained in Book 3.

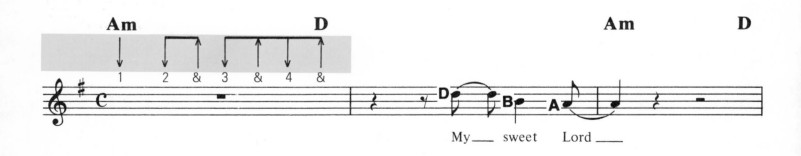

My ___ sweet Lord ___

Mm ___ my ___ Lord ___   Mm my Lord, ___

64

My Sweet Lord   Continued

N.B. The full lyric for each song can be found at the back of the book.

A Whiter Shade Of Pale

Words & Music: Keith Reid & Gary Brooker

The **F** Chord

The **F** Chord

This beautiful ballad by Procul Harum is a classic sixties pop song.

It will also introduce you to what is probably the most important major chord shape for the guitar. It uses all six strings and is therefore completely moveable. The form shown here is the **F major** required for this piece. Try making the barré right across the neck with the first finger and see if all the notes sound cleanly. Then add the second, third and fourth fingers. By now you shouldn't have any trouble with this shape.

It is worth pointing out at this stage that this chord is simply a version of the **E** chord you learnt at the

beginning of Book 1. The first finger barré is actually replacing the 'nut' of the guitar. Try it and see! You won't need chord boxes for the two other new symbols – they're just different versions of what you already know.

G/B means the new **G** chord that you learnt for 'Come Back and Stay' with a B note at the bottom. Finger your original **G** shape, leave off the second finger and play the top five strings only. For the **Am7** simply play your basic **A minor** position and remove your third finger.

It gets easier all the time, doesn't it?

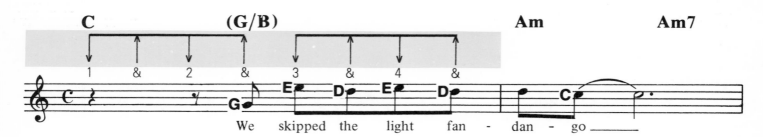

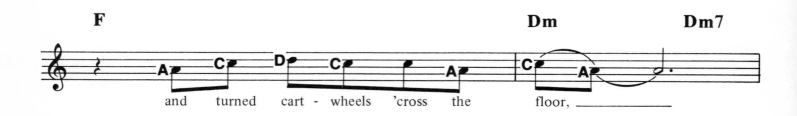

A Whiter Shade Of Pale   Continued

N.B. The full lyric for each song can be found at the back of the book.

67

The Wild Boys

Words & Music: Duran Duran

You've come across all the effects and chords used in this big hit by Duran Duran. Just keep your foot tapping and watch out for the changes in the strumming pattern.

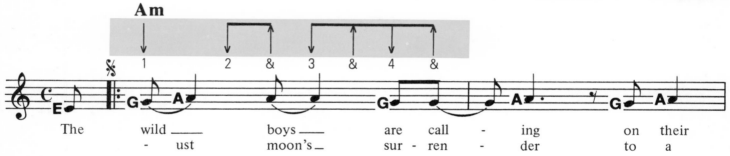

The wild ___ boys ___ are call - ing on their
- ust moon's ___ sur - ren - der to a

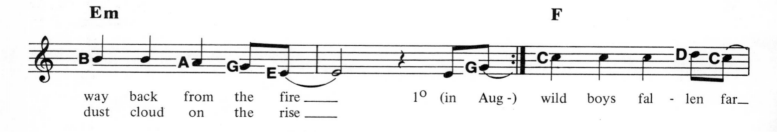

way back from the fire ___ 1° (in Aug -) wild boys fal - len far___
dust cloud on the rise ___

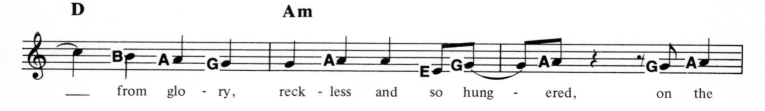

___ from glo - ry, reck - less and so hung - ered, on the

ra - zor's edge you trail, ___ be - cause there's mur - der by the

The Wild Boys   Continued

N.B. The full lyric for each song can be found at the back of the book.

Nights in White Satin

Words & Music: Justin Hayward

This song by The Moody Blues introduces you to a fast waltz tempo. It could have been written in a different form but at this stage this is the simplest way to present it.

Nights in White Satin   Continued

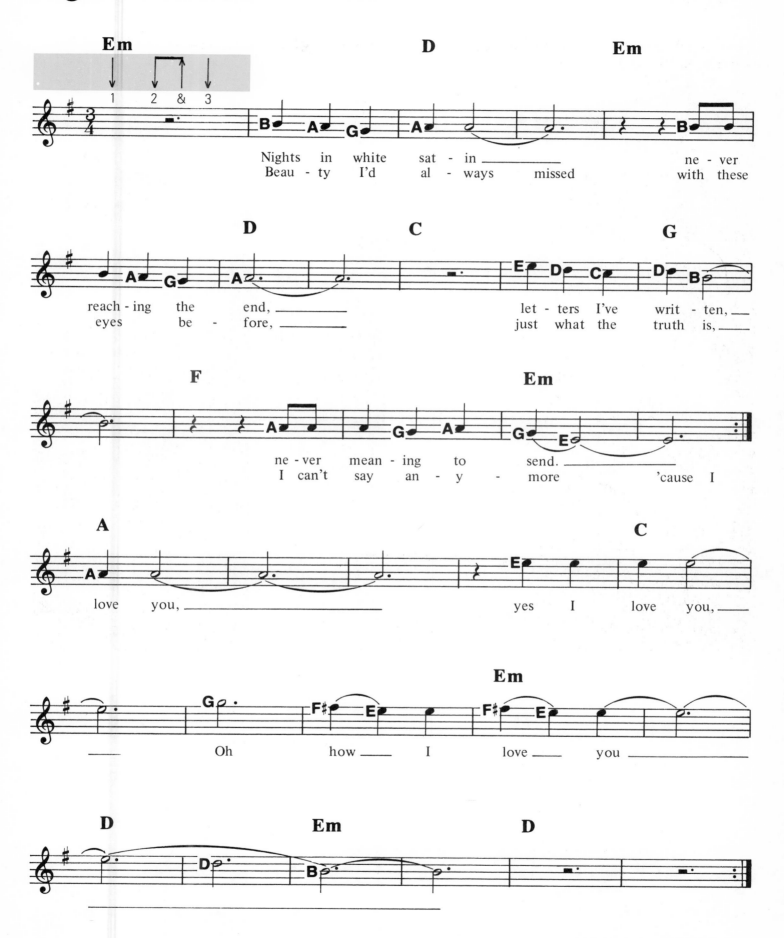

N.B. The full lyric for each song can be found at the back of the book.

Hungry Like The Wolf

Words & Music: Duran Duran

The **E Sus 4** Chord

The **E sus 4** Chord

6	5	4	3	2	1		Frets
	②	③	④				1st
							2nd
							3rd
							4th
							5th

You need only one new chord to play this Duran Duran song, and it's a simple variation of one you already know.

Simply play your basic **E** chord shape and place your fourth finger on the second fret, third string, as shown above. There is no need to remove your first finger from the string while you do this; it does not have any effect while the little finger is stopping the string and it makes changing between the chords so much simpler.

A very basic explanation of **'sus 4'** chords was given when they were first introduced in 'Honky Tonk Women'.

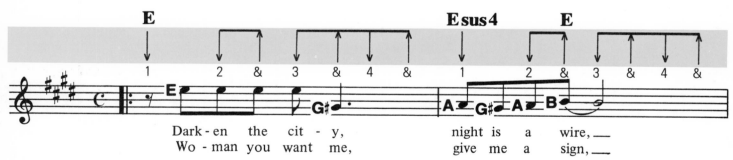

Dark - en the cit - y,   night is a wire, ___
Wo - man you want me,   give me a sign, ___

steam in the sub - way,   earth is a fire, ___ } do   do
and catch my breath - ing even clo - ser be - hind ___ }

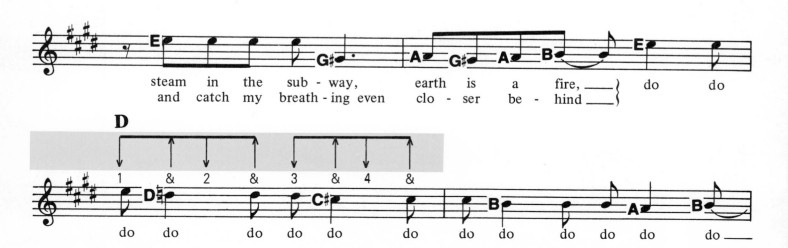

do   do   do   do   do   do   do   do   do   do   do   do ___

Hungry Like The Wolf Continued

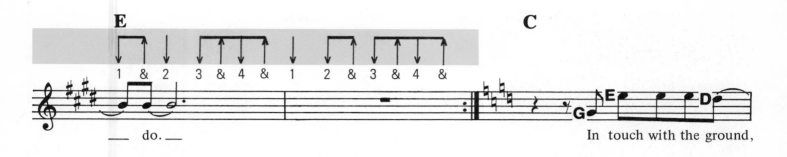

do.   In touch with the ground,

I'm on the hunt ___ I'm aft - er you. ___ Smell like I sound, ___

I'm lost in a crowd, ___ and ___ I'm hung - ry like ___ the wolf.

Strad-dle the line ___ in dis - cord and rhyme, ___ I'm on the hunt ___

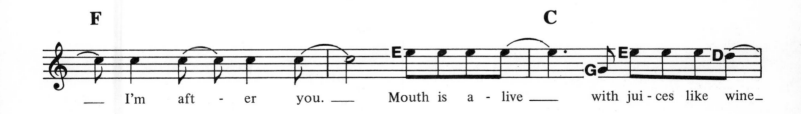

I'm aft - er you. ___ Mouth is a - live ___ with jui - ces like wine ___

and ___ I'm hung - ry like ___ the wolf. ___

N.B. The full lyric for each song can be found at the back of the book.

While My Guitar Gently Weeps

Words & Music: George Harrison

The **F♯m** Chord

6 5 4 3 2 1

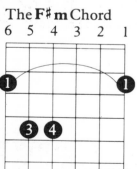

The **C♯m** Chord

6 5 4 3 2 1

Frets

1st

2nd

3rd

4th

5th

George Harrison wrote this beautiful ballad which appeared on The Beatles' 'White album'.

Two new chords appear at this stage but they are very similar to shapes you have already learnt. For the **F♯m,** start by playing your six string **F** chord and then move it up one fret. Having done this, remove your second

finger from the third string and there you have it **F♯m** minor.

Similarly, to play **C♯m** make your familiar **Bm** shape and move it up two frets. There are diagrams for you if this is not clear but by now moveable chords should present no problem.

While My Guitar Gently Weeps Continued

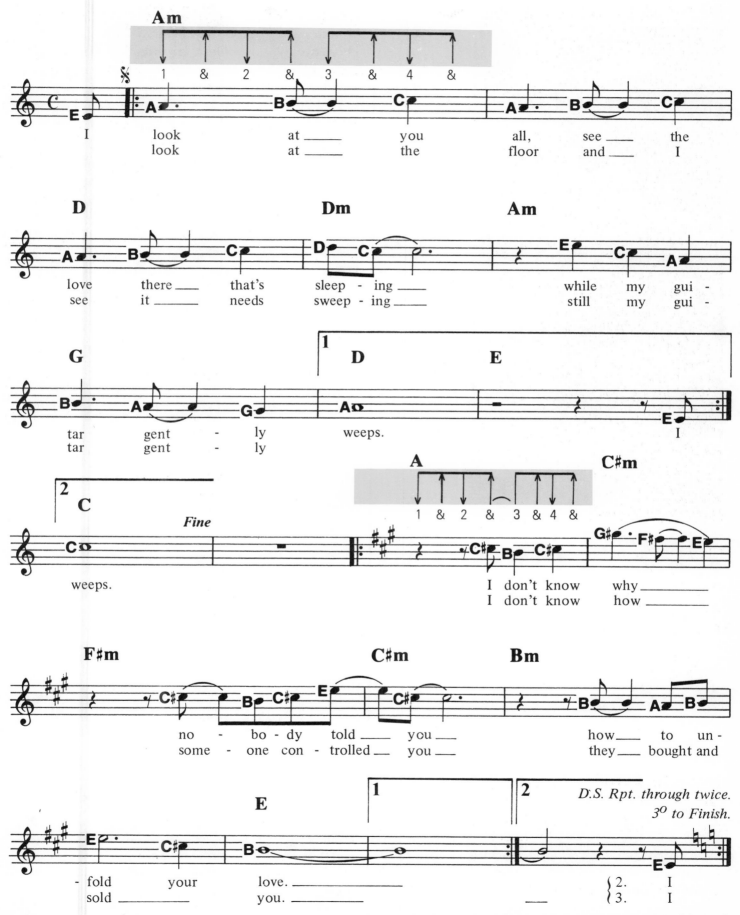

N.B. The full lyric for each song can be found at the back of the book.

Pinball Wizard

Words & Music: Peter Townshend

The **A Sus 4** Chord

The **A sus 4** Chord

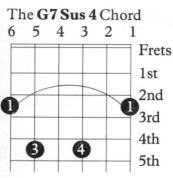

The **G7 Sus 4** Chord

This hit by The Who was taken from their opera 'Tommy' and features one of Pete Townshend's classic chord progressions. There are three new **'Sus 4'** chords for this piece but you have only been given two of them. The reason for this is that the **G7 sus 4** shape is a moveable chord and to play **F7 sus 4** you simply move it two frets down the fretboard. This should not need any further explanation but if you are in any difficulty read the section on the **F** chord which was introduced in 'A Whiter Shade Of Pale.'

The rhythm for the verse is much simpler than it looks, and you will soon recognise the phrase. The figure in bars 9 and 11 is another very common pattern. Just remember to tap your foot on 1,2,3,4 and play the chords on the '&'.

Ev - er since I was a young boy I played the sil - ver ball from

So - ho down to Brigh - ton, I must have played em' all, but I

ain't seen no - thing like him in an - y a - muse - ment hall, that

76

Pinball Wizard Continued

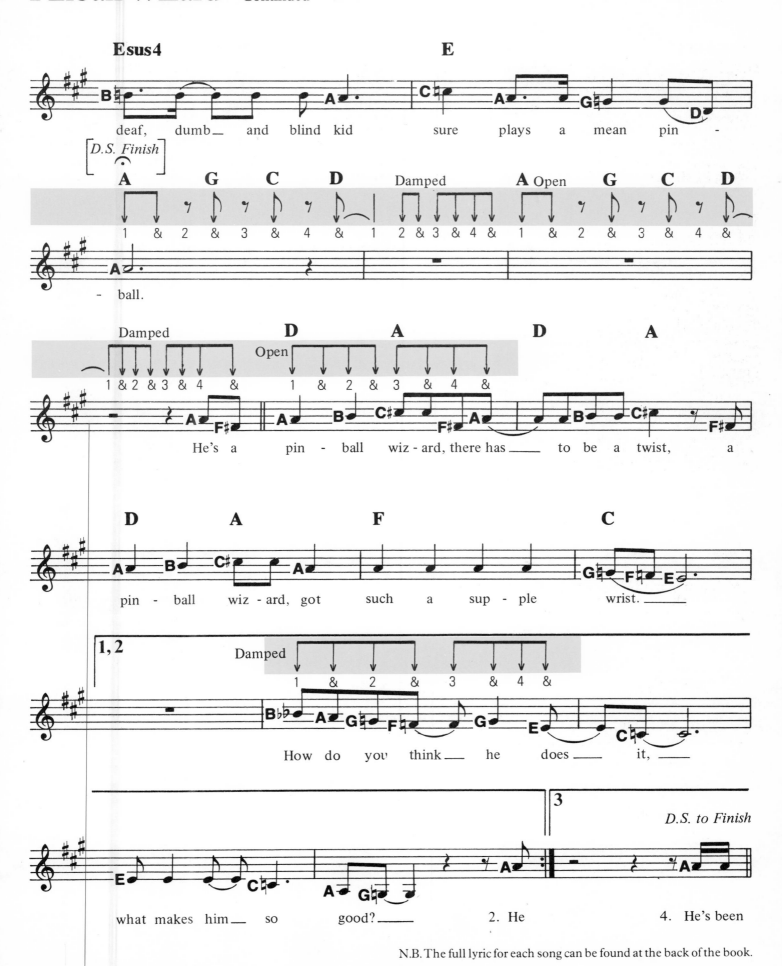

Come Back And Stay

Since you've been gone
I shut my eyes
And I fantasise
That you're here with me.
Will you ever return?
I won't be satisfied till you're by my side.
Don't wait any longer
Why don't you come back, please hurry.
Why don't you come back, please hurry,
Come back and stay for good this time,
Come back and stay for good this time.

When you said goodbye
I was trying to hide what I felt inside
Until it passed me by.
You said you'd return,
You said that you'd be mine till the end of time.
Well don't wait any longer.

Since you've been gone
I opened my eyes and I realised
What we had together.
Will you ever return?
Or have you changed your mind, if you wanna stay mine
Just love me forever.

Moonlight Shadow

The last time ever she saw him carried away by a
    moonlight shadow,
He passed on worried and warning carried away by a
    moonlight shadow,
Lost in a riddle that Saturday night far away on the other
    side
He was caught in the middle of a desperate fight,
And she couldn't find how to push through.

The trees that whisper in the evening
Carried away by a moonlight shadow
Sing a song of sorrow and grieving
Carried away by a moonlight shadow.
All she saw was the silhouette of a gun
Far away on the other side
He was shot six times by a man on the run
And she couldn't find how to push it through.

Four a.m. in the morning
Carried away by a moonlight shadow
I watch your vision forming
Carried away by a moonlight shadow.
The stars move slowly in a silvery light
Far away on the other side
Will you come to talk to me this night
But she couldn't find how to push through.

I stay, I pray see you in heaven far away,
I stay, I pray see you in heaven one day.

Caught in the middle of a hundred and five
The night was heavy and the air was alive
But she couldn't find how to push through.

Hey Joe

Hey Joe, where ya goin' with that gun in your hand?
I said hey Joe, where ya goin' with that gun in your hand?
I'm going out to find my woman now.
She's been runnin' round with some other man.
I said I'm going out and find my woman
She's been runnin' round with some other man.

Hey Joe, tell me what are you gonna do?
Hey Joe, tell me what are you gonna do?
Well I guess I'll shoot my woman, that's what I'll do.
Well I guess I'll shoot 'em both before I'm through.

Hey Joe, tell me where are you gonna go?
Hey Joe, tell me where are you gonna go?
Well, I think I'll go down to my favourite place, Mexico
Well, I think I'll go down to where a man can be free
And there ain't gonna be no hangman's ropes
Gonna be put around me.

Honky Tonk Women

I met a gin soaked, bar-room queen in Memphis,
She tried to take me upstairs for a ride,
She had to heave me right across her shoulder
'Cause I just can't seem to drink you off my mind.

Chorus:

It's the Honky Tonk Women
Gimme, gimme, gimme the honky tonk blues.

I played a divorceé in New York City
I had to put up some kind of a fight.
The lady then she covered me with roses,
She blew my nose and then she blew my mind.

Chorus

Light My Fire

You know that it would be untrue,
You know that I would be a liar
If I was to say to you
Girl, we couldn't get much higher.

Chorus:
Come on, baby, light my fire.
Come on, baby, light my fire.
Try to set the night on fire.

The time to hesitate is through,
No time to wallow in the mire,
Try now we can only lose
And our love become a funeral pyre.

Chorus.

So Far Away

Here I am again in this mean old town,
And you're so far away from me.
Now where are you when the sun goes down
You're so far away from me.
I'm tired of being in love and being all alone
When you're so far away from me.
I'm tired of making out on the telephone
'Cause you're so far away from me.
And I get so tired when I have to explain
When you're so far away from me.
See you've been in the sun and I've been in the rain
And you're so far away from me.

You're so far away from me,
You're so far I just can't see.
You're so far away from me,
You're so far away from me, alright,
You're so far away from me.
(Fade)

I Shot The Sheriff

I shot the sheriff, but I did not shoot the deputy.
I shot the sheriff, but I did not shoot the deputy.
All around in my hometown they're trying to track me
    down.
They say they want to bring me in guilty for the killing of
    a deputy.
For the killing of a deputy, but I say:

I shot the sheriff but I swear it was in self-defence.
I shot the sheriff and they say it is a capital offence.
Sheriff John Brown always hated me: for what, I don't
    know
Every time that I plant a seed he said kill it before it grow.
He said kill it before it grow, but I say:

I shot the sheriff but I swear it was in self-defence.
I shot the sheriff but I swear it was in self-defence.
Freedom came my way one day and I started out of town.
All of a sudden I see Sheriff John Brown aiming to shoot
    me down,
So I shot, I shot him down, but I say:

I shot the sheriff but I did not shoot the deputy.
I shot the sheriff but I did not shoot no deputy.
Reflexes got the better of me and what is to be must be.
Every day the bucket goes to the well but one day the
    bottom will drop out,
Yes, one day the bottom will drop out, but I say:

(Rpt. verse 1 and fade)

(This Could Be) The Last Time

Well, I told you once and I told you twice,
But you never listen to my advice,
You don't try very hard to please me,
With what you know it should be easy.

This could be the last time,
This could be the last time,
May be the last time
I don't know, Oh no, Oh no.

Well, I'm sorry girl but I can't stay
Feelin' like I do today.
It's too much pain and too much sorrow,
Guess I'll feel the same tomorrow.

Well, I told you once and I told you twice,
That someone else will have to pay the price.
But here's a chance to change your mind,
'Cause I'll be gone a long, long time.

Don't Pay The Ferryman

It was late at night on the open road,
Speeding like a man on the run,
A life time spent preparing for the journey.
He was closer now and the search was on,
Reading from a map in the mind.
Yes, there's the ragged hill, and there's a boat on the
river.

And when the rain came down
He heard a wild dog howl.
There were voices in the night.
(Don't do it!)
Voices out of sight,
(Don't do it!)
Too many men have failed before,
Whatever you do
Don't pay the ferryman,
Don't even fix a price.
Don't pay the ferryman
Until he gets you to the other side.

In the roaming mist then he gets on board,
Now there'll be no turning back,
Beware the hooded old man at the rudder.
And then the lightning flashed and the thunder roared,
And people calling out his name,
And dancing bows that jabbered and a' moaned on the
water.
And then the ferryman said there is trouble ahead
So you must pay me now
(Don't do it!)
You must pay me now
(Don't do it!)
And still that voice came through the air
Whatever you do ...

My Sweet Lord

My sweet Lord, mm my Lord, mm my Lord,
I really want to see you.
Really want to be with you.
Really want to see you Lord,
But it takes so long, my Lord.

My sweet Lord, mm my Lord, mm my Lord,
I really want to know you.
Really want to go with you.
Really want to show you, Lord,
That it won't take long, my Lord.

My sweet Lord, mm my Lord, my sweet Lord,
I really want to see you.
Really want to see you.
Really want to see you Lord.
Really want to see you, Lord,
But it takes so long my Lord,
My sweet Lord, mm my Lord, my, my, my Lord, my
sweet Lord.

A Whiter Shade Of Pale

We skipped the light fandango and turned cartwheels
'cross the floor
I was feeling kind of seasick
But the crowd called out for more,
The room was humming harder
As the ceiling flew away
When we called out for another drink
The waiter brought a tray.
And so it was that later
As the miller told his tale
That her face at first just ghostly turned a whiter shade
of pale.

The Wild Boys

The wild boys are calling
On their way back from the fire,
In August moon's surrender
To a dust cloud on the rise.
Wild boys fallen far from glory,
Reckless and so hungered,
On the razor's edge you trail,
Because there's murder by the roadside
In a sore afraid new world.
They tried to break us,
Looks like they'll try again.

Chorus:
Wild boys never lose it,
Wild boys never choose this way,
Wild boys never close your eyes,
Wild boys always shine.

You got sirens for a welcome,
There's bloodstain for your pain,
And your telephone's been ringing
While you're dancing in the rain.
Wild boys wonder where is glory,
Where is all you angels,
Now the figureheads have fell.
And lovers war with arrows
Over secrets they could tell.
They tried to tame you,
Looks like they'll try again ..

Chorus.

Nights In White Satin

Nights in white satin never reaching the end.
Letters I've written never meaning to send.
Beauty I'd always missed with these eyes before,
Just what the truth is I can't say any more,
'Cause I love you,
Yes I love
Oh, how I love you

Gazing at people, some hand in hand,
Just what I'm going through they can't understand.
Some try to tell me thoughts they cannot defend,
Just what you want to be, you'll be in the end,
And I love you,
Yes, I love you,
Oh, how I love you.
How I love you.

Hungry Like The Wolf

Darken the city, night is a wire,
Steam in the subway, earth is a fire,
Do do do do do do do do
Do do do do do do do.

Woman you want me, give me a sign,
And catch my breathing even closer behind
Do do do ...
Do do do ...

Chorus:
In touch with the ground, I'm on the hunt, I'm after you,
Smell like I sound, I'm lost in a crowd,
And I'm hungry like the wolf
Straddle the line in discord and rhyme
I'm on the hunt, I'm after you.
Mouth is alive with juices like wine
And I'm hungry like the wolf.

Stalked in the forest, too close to hide,
I'll be upon you by the moonlight side,
Do do do ...
High blood drumming on the skin, it's so tight,
You feel my heat, I'm just a moment behind
Do do do ...

Chorus:
In touch with the ground, I'm on the hunt I'm after you
Scent and a sound, I'm lost and I'm found,
And I'm hungry like the wolf
Strut on a line, it's discord and rhyme
I howl and I whine, I'm after you.
Mouth is alive, all running inside
And I'm hungry like the wolf.

Final Chorus:
I break from the crowd, I'm on the hunt, I'm after you.
I smell like I sound, I'm lost and I'm found
And I'm hungry like the wolf.
Strut on a line, it's discord and rhyme
Mouth is alive with juices like wine
And I'm hungry like the wolf.

And I'm hungry like the wolf.

While My Guitar Gently Weeps

I look at you all see the love there that's sleeping
While my guitar gently weeps
I look at the floor and I see it needs sweeping
Still my guitar gently weeps
I don't know why nobody told you how to unfold your
    love
I don't know how someone controlled you they bought
    and sold you
I look at you all see the love there that's sleeping
While my guitar gently weeps
I look at you all
Still my guitar gently weeps.

I look at the world and I notice it's turning
While my guitar gently weeps
With every mistake we must surely be learning
Still my guitar gently weeps
I don't know how you were diverted you were perverted
    too
I don't know how you were inverted no one altered you
I look at you all see the love there that's sleeping
While my guitar gently weeps
I look at you all
Still my guitar gently weeps.

Pinball Wizard

Ever since I was a young boy I played the silver ball;
From Soho down to Brighton I must have played 'em all,
But I ain't seen nothin' like him in any amusement hall.
That deaf, dumb and blind kid sure plays a mean
    pinball.

Chorus:
He's a pinball wizard there has to be a twist,
A pinball wizard, got such a supple wrist
How do you think he does it? (I don't know)
What makes him so good?

He stands like a statue, becomes part of the machine,
Feelin' all the bumpers, always playin' clean,
Plays by intuition, the digit counters fall
That deaf, dumb and blind kid sure plays a mean
    pinball.

Chorus.

Ain't got no distractions, can't hear no buzzes and bells,
Don't see no lights a flashin' plays by sense of smell,
Always gets a replay never seen him fall.
That deaf, dumb and blind kid sure plays a mean
    pinball.

I thought I was the body table king,
But I just handed my pinball crown to him.
How do you think he does it? (I don't know)
What makes him so good?

He's been on my fav'rite table, he can beat my best,
His disciples lead him in and he just does the rest.
He's got crazy flippin' fingers, never seen him fall
That deaf, dumb and blind kid sure plays a mean
    pinball.

The Complete
Rock & Pop
Guitar Player
by Mick Barker, Rick Cardinali, Roger Day.
Book 3

Songs included in this book

Rio   Words & Music: Duran Duran

For 'Rio' you will need two new chords, they are **A** with a **C#** in the bass which is written **A/C#** and **B major.**

The **A/C#** Chord

The **A/C#** Chord

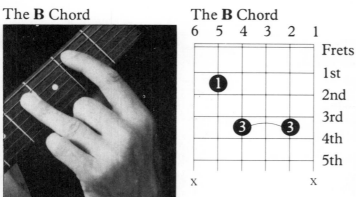

The **B** Chord

The **B** Chord

You will notice that the first strum mark for the verse rhythm has a dot after it. The dot means that the note preceding it is half as long again in duration. Thus, the strum pattern is counted and played as below. (Remember the tie sign means that you don't play the second of the tied notes).

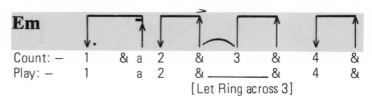

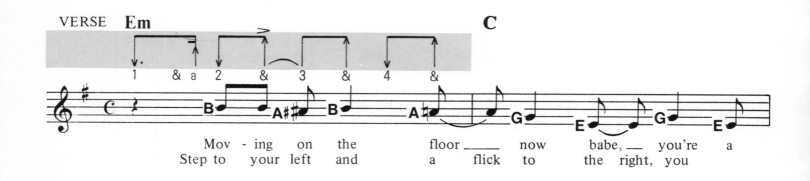

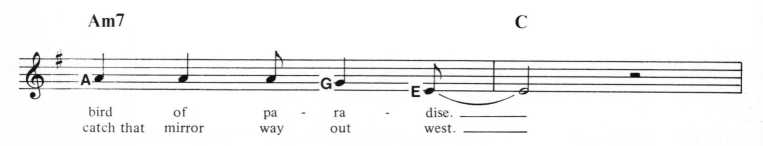

82

Rio
Continued

N.B. The full lyric for each song can be found at the back of the book.

Without You

Words & Music: Peter Ham & Tom Evans

The **D seventh** chord

The **D7** chord

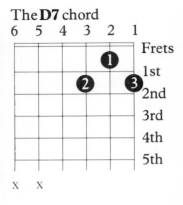

The **Am maj 7th** chord

The **Am♭7** chord

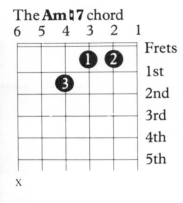

The strum pattern for this Harry Nilsson hit song is easy, but there are three new chords to learn. **G6** is easy to play and requires no chord box because you hold down your 'old' **G** shape and simply remove your 3rd finger, letting the top four strings 'ring open'.

The **Aminor maj7** and **D7** chords are illustrated in the chord boxes.

This song has a $\frac{2}{4}$ (two four) bar in the chorus. Simply count the 1 & 2 & as shown and return to your normal 1 & 2 & 3 & 4 & when you take the sign (𝄋) back to the top of the piece.

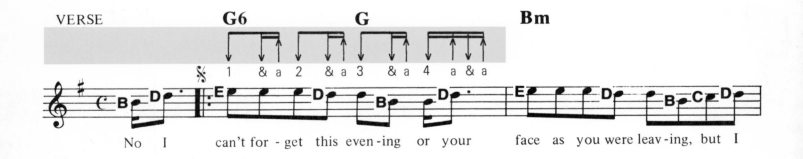

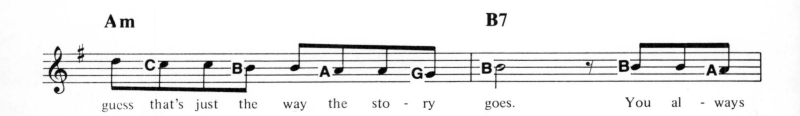

Without You Continued

N.B. The full lyric for each song can be found at the back of the book.

Alright Now
Words & Music: Paul Rodgers and Andy Fraser

The **D/A** Chord

The **D/A** Chord

The **D9 Sus 4** Chord

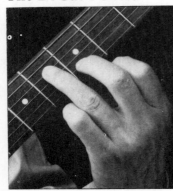

The **D9 Sus 4** Chord

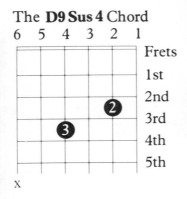

These two new chords are all you need to learn in order to play this classic hit by Free, featuring Paul Kossof on guitar. The **D9 sus 4** is not a widely used chord, but is very effective in the context of this famous intro. Remember that ✗ means that you damp the strings for a percussive 'clicky' sound. Another way of damping the

strings, is to lift your left hand slightly from the fret-board (while still maintaining the chord shape), so that your fingertips rest lightly on the strings.

You should try and arrange your hand so that none of the strings are ringing open. Then when you strum you will hear a damped sound. This method is quicker to implement than the 'side of hand' technique and should be used for this intro. Don't forget to go back to open strums when the marks change from ✗ to ↓ .

INTRO RIFF

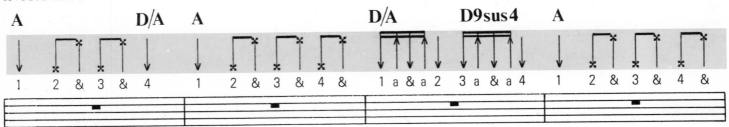

Alright Now Continued

N.B. The full lyric for each song can be found at the back of the book.

Goodbye Yellow Brick Road

Words & Music: Elton John & Bernie Taupin

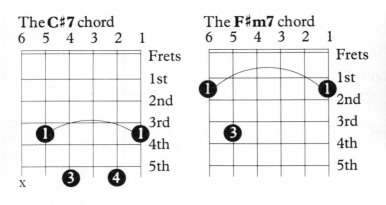

The **C#7** chord

The **F#m7** chord

The new chords in this hit by Elton John are all variations on what you have already learnt except for the **C#7** shown above, and even that shape is a version of the **B** chord you played for 'Rio'. It takes its name from the note fingered on the 5th string. The **F#m7** is your basic six-string major chord shape fingered at the second fret. To turn your familiar **F#m** into **F#m7** simply remove your 4th finger from the 4th string.

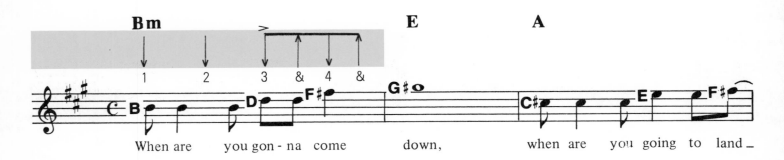

When are you gon-na come down, when are you going to land —

— I should have stayed — on the farm, — should have lis -

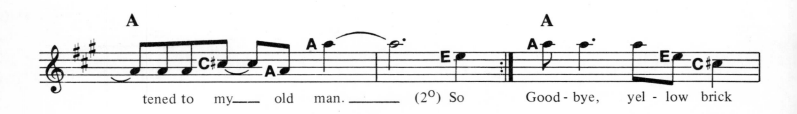

tened to my — old man. — (2°) So Good - bye, yel - low brick

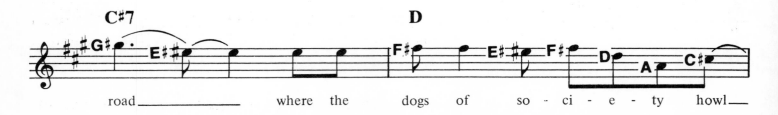

road _____ where the dogs of so - ci - e - ty howl —

Goodbye Yellow Brick Road   Continued

you can't plant me in your pent - house, ___ I'm

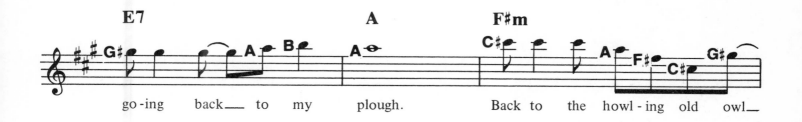

go - ing back___ to my plough. Back to the howl - ing old owl___

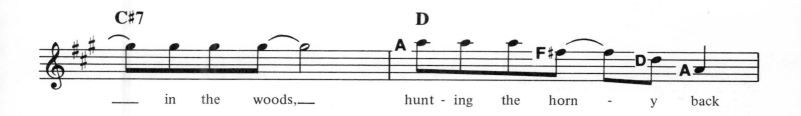

___ in the woods, ___ hunt - ing the horn - y back

toad. Oh I've fin - ally de - ci - ded my

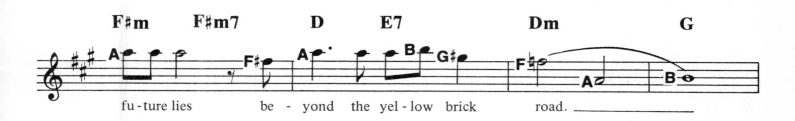

fu - ture lies be - yond the yel - low brick road. ___

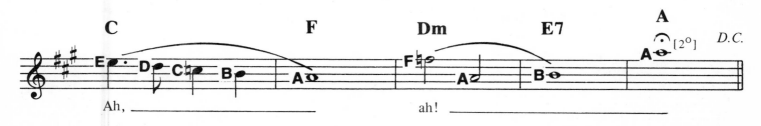

Ah, ___ ah! ___

N.B. The full lyric for each song can be found at the back of the book.

Tonight I Celebrate My Love

Words & Music: Michael Masser and Gerry Goffin

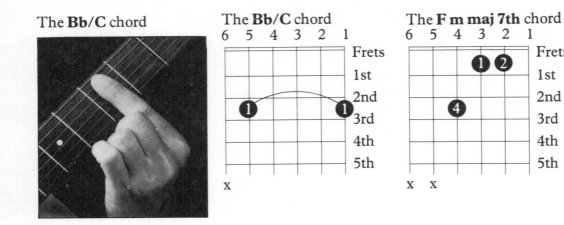

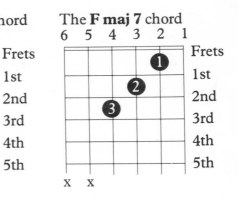

The **Fminor maj7th (Fm♭7), Fmaj7th and B♭/C** chords are illustrated in the relevant boxes. Another chord that you will need for this piece is **C7** which does not need a chord box. It can be played simply by

holding down the **C♯7** moveable chord shape which you learnt in 'Yellow Brick Road' and sliding it one fret down the board (away from you.)

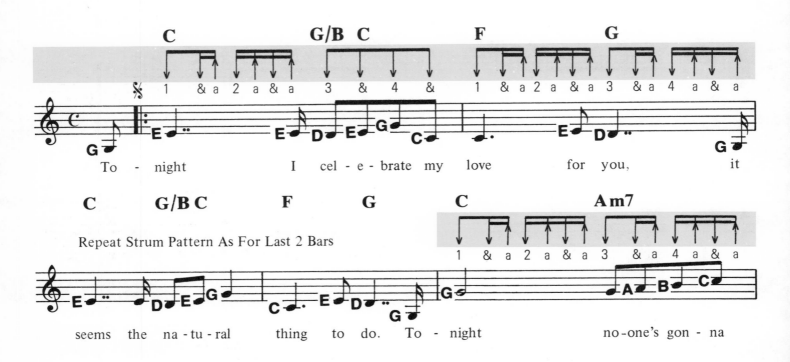

Repeat Strum Pattern As For Last 2 Bars

Tonight I Celebrate My Love Continued

N.B. The full lyric for each song can be found at the back of the book.

Y.M.C.A.
Words & Music: J. Morali, H. Belolo & V. Willis

The D minor 6th chord

The Dm6 chord

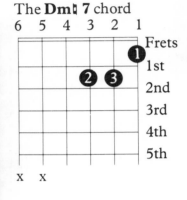

The Dm maj 7 chord

The Dm♭7 chord

Once you have mastered the two new chords try this chord progression, strumming slowly at first. You will recognise it as a 'magic moment' from the chorus of 'Y.M.C.A.'

Next try strumming this rhythm, which occurs at the end of each verse of 'Y.M.C.A.'

Notice how the words coincide with the accented strums.

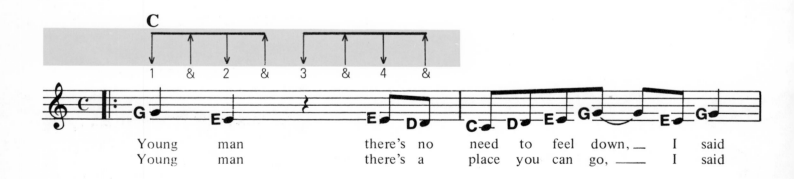

Young man there's no need to feel down, __ I said
Young man there's a place you can go, ___ I said

young man pick your - self off the ground, __ I said
young man when you're short on your dough, __ you can

Y.M.C.A. Continued

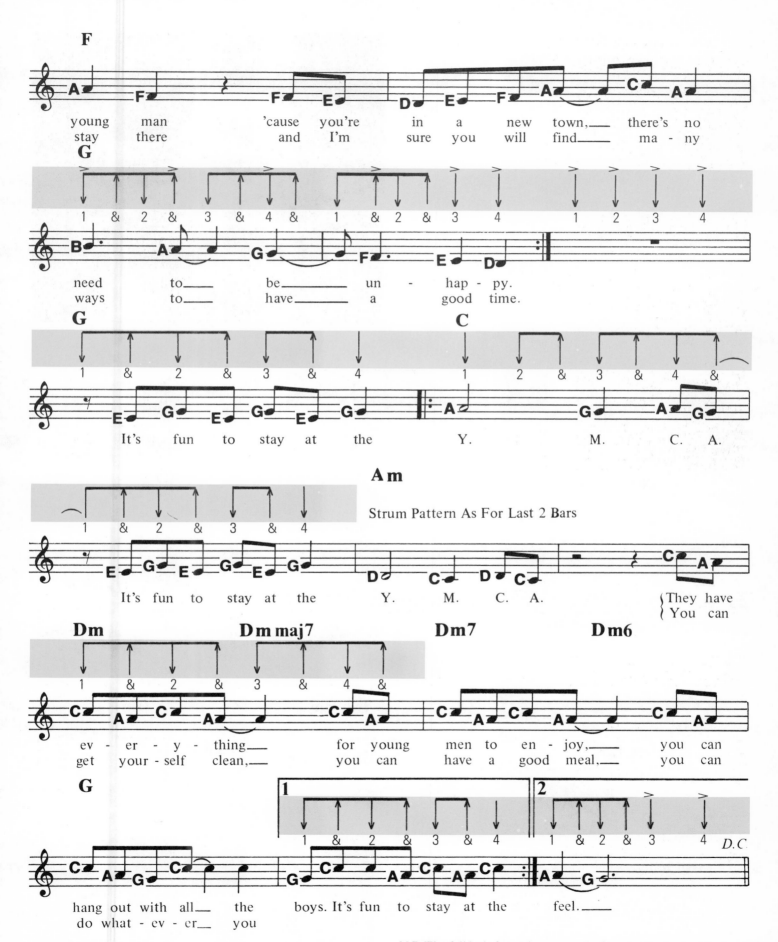

young man 'cause you're in a new town,___ there's no
stay there and I'm sure you will find___ ma-ny

need to___ be___ un - hap - py.
ways to___ have___ a good time.

It's fun to stay at the Y. M. C. A.

Strum Pattern As For Last 2 Bars

It's fun to stay at the Y. M. C. A. { They have
{ You can

ev - er - y - thing___ for young men to en - joy,___ you can
get your - self clean,___ you can have a good meal,___ you can

hang out with all___ the boys. It's fun to stay at the feel.___
do what - ev - er___ you

N.B. The full lyric for each song can be found at the back of the book.

© Copyright 1978 Zomba Publishers Ltd., for the UK, Northern Ireland & Eire.
All rights reserved. International copyright secured.

I Just Called To Say I Love You   Words & Music: Stevie Wonder

Here is a song which will help you to revise some of the chords you have learnt.

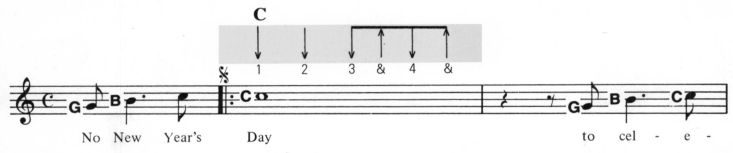

No New Year's Day   to cel - e -

- brate,   no choco - late co - vered can - dy hearts

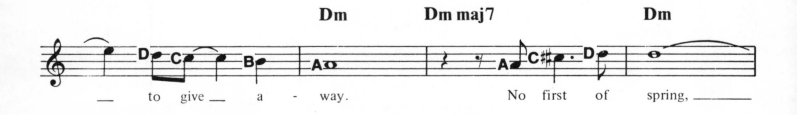

___ to give ___ a - way.   No first of spring, ___

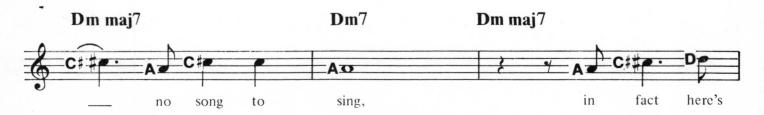

___ no song to   sing,   in fact here's

94

I Just Called To Say I Love You   Continued

N.B. The full lyric for each song can be found at the back of the book.

Bright Eyes

Words & Music: Mike Batt

The **C# dim** chord

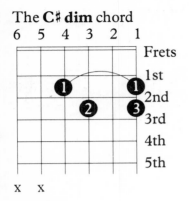

In this song there is a **C#** diminished chord (**C#°**). It is exactly the same shape as the **G#** diminished (**G#°**) which you learnt in order to play 'My Sweet Lord' (Book 2). So, to play **C#** diminished, you should position your fingers in the **G#°** shape and then slide them one fret down the board (away from you). Exactly why this works with diminished chords is explained at the end of the book, but see if you can guess the answer by remembering what was said about diminished chords in 'My Sweet Lord'.

This song has a $\frac{2}{4}$ (two four) bar in the chorus. Simply count the 1 & 2 & as shown and return to your normal 1 & 2 & 3 & 4 & on the word 'dream'.

Once you have mastered the song, try out your own strum patterns.

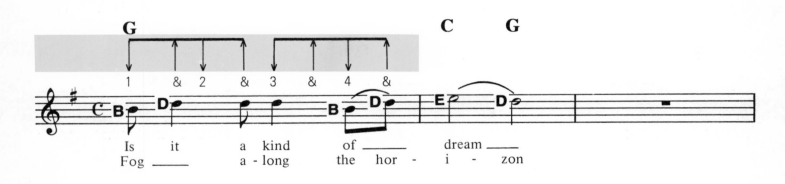

Is it a kind of ___ dream ___
Fog ___ a - long the hor - i - zon

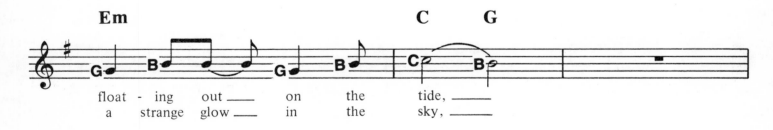

float - ing out ___ on the tide, ___
a strange glow ___ in the sky, ___

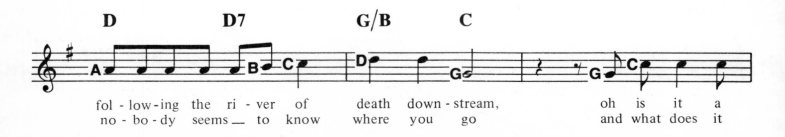

fol - low - ing the ri - ver of death down - stream, oh is it a
no - bo - dy seems ___ to know where you go and what does it

96

Bright Eyes Continued

Going Down Town Tonight

Words & Music: Guy Johnson

Getting the right effect for this Status Quo song is very easy. When you play the bars with all down strum markings simply damp the strings with the side of your hand. This technique was explained fully earlier in the series. As a final point, try and concentrate more on the lower strings of the instrument and you'll get that authentic chunky Status Quo sound.

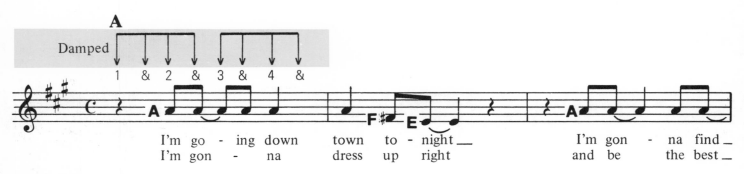

I'm go - ing down town to - night __ I'm gon - na find __
I'm gon - na dress up right and be the best __

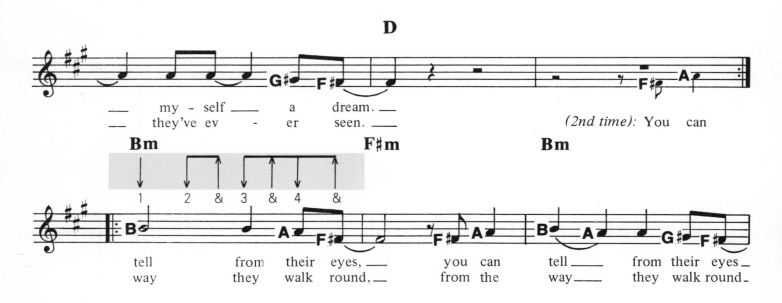

__ my - self __ a dream. __
__ they've ev - er seen. __

(2nd time): You can

tell from their eyes, __ you can tell __ from their eyes __
way they walk round, __ from the way __ they walk round __

__ that they're nev - er __ im - pressed, __ that they're
__ they are used to __ the best, __ oh, are

Going Down Town Tonight   Continued

N.B. The full lyric for each song can be found at the back of the book.

Killing Me Softly

Words: Norman Gimbel   Music: Charles Fox

The **Bb** chord

The **Bb** chord

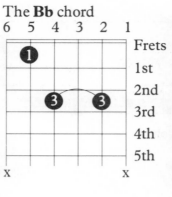

You have only one new chord to learn in order to play this Roberta Flack hit.

The **B♭** chord is exactly the same shape as the **B** chord you learnt to play in the song 'Rio'. Simply position your fingers in the **B** shape and slide them one fret down the fretboard (away from you), so that your 1st finger rests on the 1st fret of the 5th string, and your 3rd finger is a 3-string barré on the 3rd fret of the 4th, 3rd and 2nd strings. Like the **B** chord, it takes its name from the note fingered on the 5th string.

I heard — he sang — a good — song, I heard he had—

— a style. And so— I came —— to see —— him to

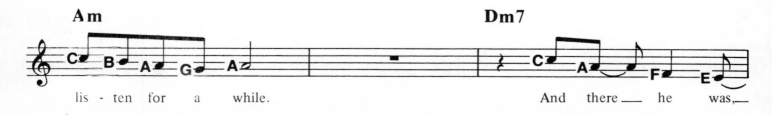

lis - ten for a while. And there — he was,—

Killing Me Softly Continued

this young boy, a stran - ger to my eyes

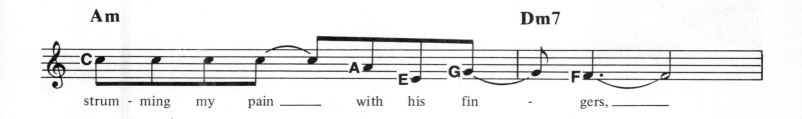

strum - ming my pain with his fin - gers,

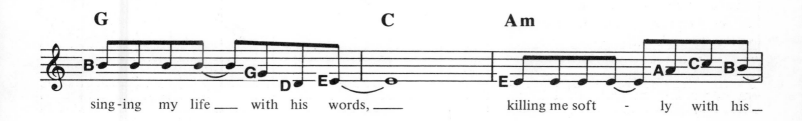

sing -ing my life with his words, killing me soft - ly with his

song, kill - ing me soft - ly with his song, tell - ing my whole

life with his words, kill - ing me soft - ly

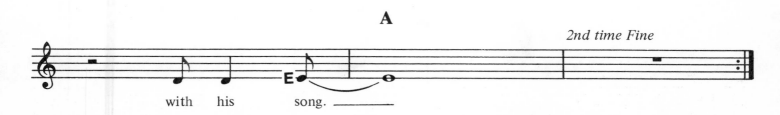

with his song.

N.B. The full lyric for each song can be found at the back of the book.

Hold Me Now

Words & Music: Tom Bailey, Alannah Currie and Joe Leeway

The C add 9 chord

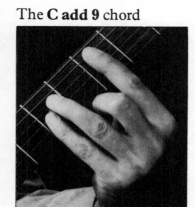

The C add 9 chord

6 5 4 3 2 1

Frets
1st
2nd
3rd
4th
5th

x

There is a new chord to learn for this hit by The Thompson Twins. The **Cadd 9** (**C+9**) is a moveable chord shape, which has been used effectively in many contemporary songs, and you will almost certainly recognise the sound. The chord takes its name from the note stopped by your 1st finger on the 5th string. The accompaniment for the last five bars of the song is written out in tablature.

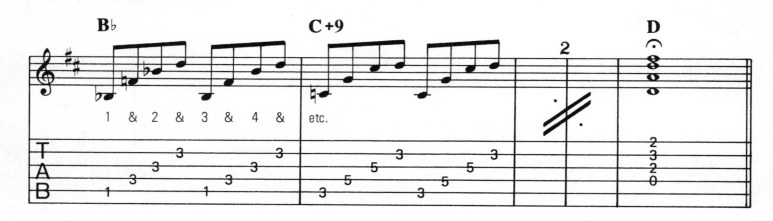

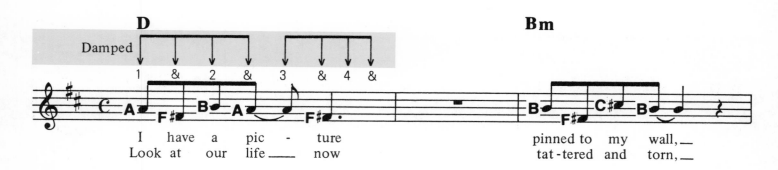

I have a pic - ture   pinned to my wall, ___
Look at our life ___ now   tat -tered and torn, ___

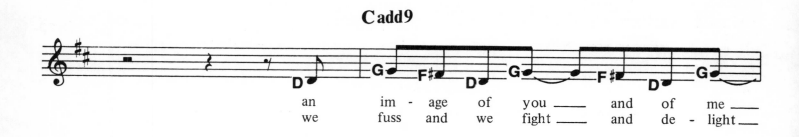

an im - age of you ___ and of me ___
we fuss and we fight ___ and de - light ___

102

Hold Me Now Continued

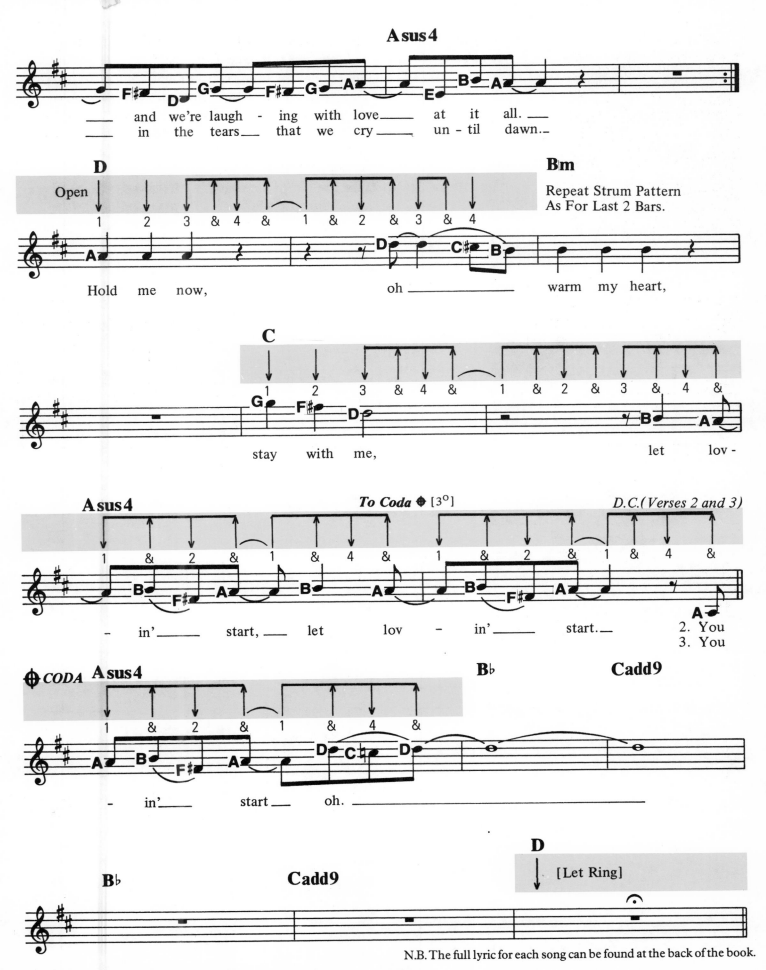

Knowing Me Knowing You

Words & Music: Benny Andersson,
Stig Anderson & Bjorn Ulvaeus

The **B add 9** chord

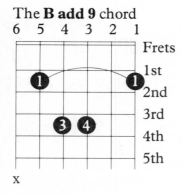

x

You will notice a **Badd 9** (**B+9**) in the music for this Abba song. It occurs just before the chorus on the word 'Goodbye'.

This chord is exactly the same shape as the **C+9** which you learnt in order to play 'Hold Me Now'. Simply position your fingers in the **C+9** shape and slide them one fret down the fretboard (away from you).

Note that the second to last bar is in $\frac{2}{4}$ (two four) time, which means that you count . . 1 & 2 & only , before returning to $\frac{4}{4}$ time count . . . 1 & 2 & 3 & 4 & as you play the **D** chord in the last bar on the word 'do'. You will recognise the solo riff in the tablature from the famous record.

SOLO RIFF IN TABLATURE

Knowing Me Knowing You   Continued

N.B. The full lyric for each song can be found at the back of the book.

Only You
Words & Music: Vincent Clarke

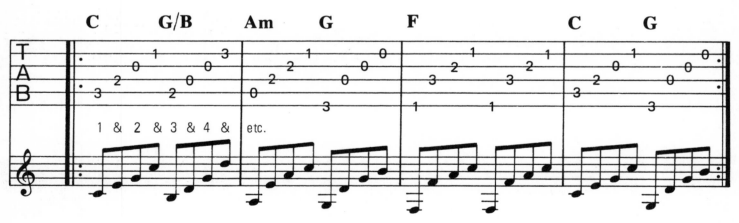

'Only You' was a hit for both Yazoo and The Flying Pickets. You can simply follow the chord symbols and strum marks as usual or you can learn a stylish new way to accompany a song.

Written above in notation and tablature is an example of what is called Arpeggio style chord playing. What it means is that instead of strumming a chord the notes are sounded individually one after another. The effect is both evocative and resonant.

You will find that if you play the four bar section twice, it fits with the first eight bars of the tune. When you reach the **F** chord at the beginning of bar 9, simply strum as shown, returning to the Arpeggio pattern for the second verse.

Only You   Continued

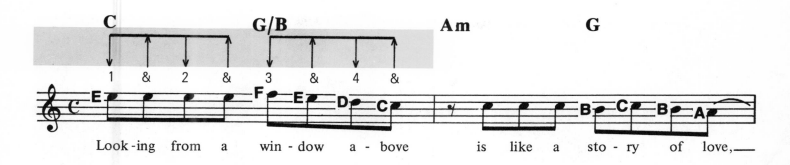

C   **G/B**   **Am**   **G**

1 & 2 & 3 & 4 &

Look -ing from a win - dow a -bove   is like a sto - ry of love,

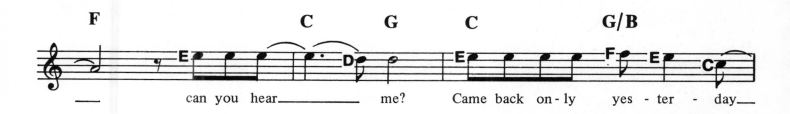

F   **C**   **G**   **C**   **G/B**

— can you hear_____ me?   Came back on -ly yes - ter - day—

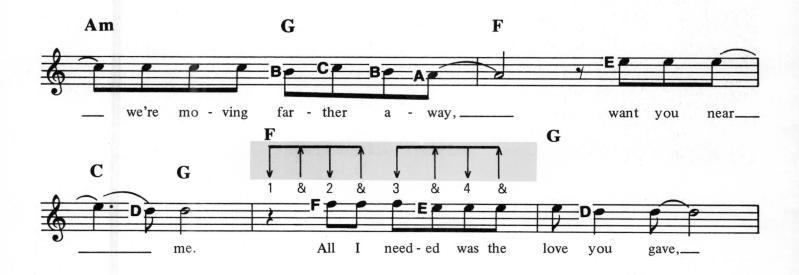

Am   **G**   **F**

— we're mo - ving far - ther a - way,_____   want you near—

F   **G**

C   **G**

1 & 2 & 3 & 4 &

——— me.   All I need - ed was the love you gave,—

C   **F**   **F**

all I need - ed for an - oth - er day,—   and all I ev - er knew—

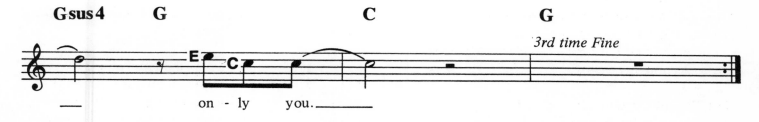

G sus 4   **G**   **C**   **G**

3rd time Fine

— on - ly you.—

N.B. The full lyric for each song can be found at the back of the book.

Easy Lover

Words: Phil Collins Music: Phil Collins, Philip Bailey and Nathan East

This Phil Collins hit uses no new chords but watch out for the strum patterns. Remember that B means you play the note B (found on the 5th string, 2nd fret) and not the whole chord.

There is a very effective quick chord change from **D** to **Em** on the words 'better forget it'. It is easy to do provided you remember that the change to the **D** chord comes on the syllable .. 'ter' of the word 'better', and the change to **Em** comes on the syllable .. 'get' of the word 'forget'.

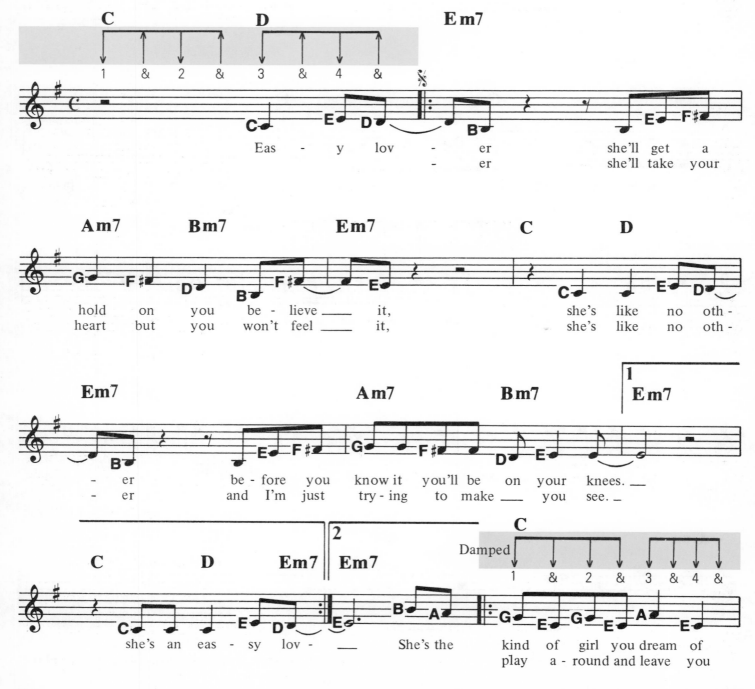

Easy Lover Continued

N.B. The full lyric for each song can be found at the back of the book.

Chord Revision

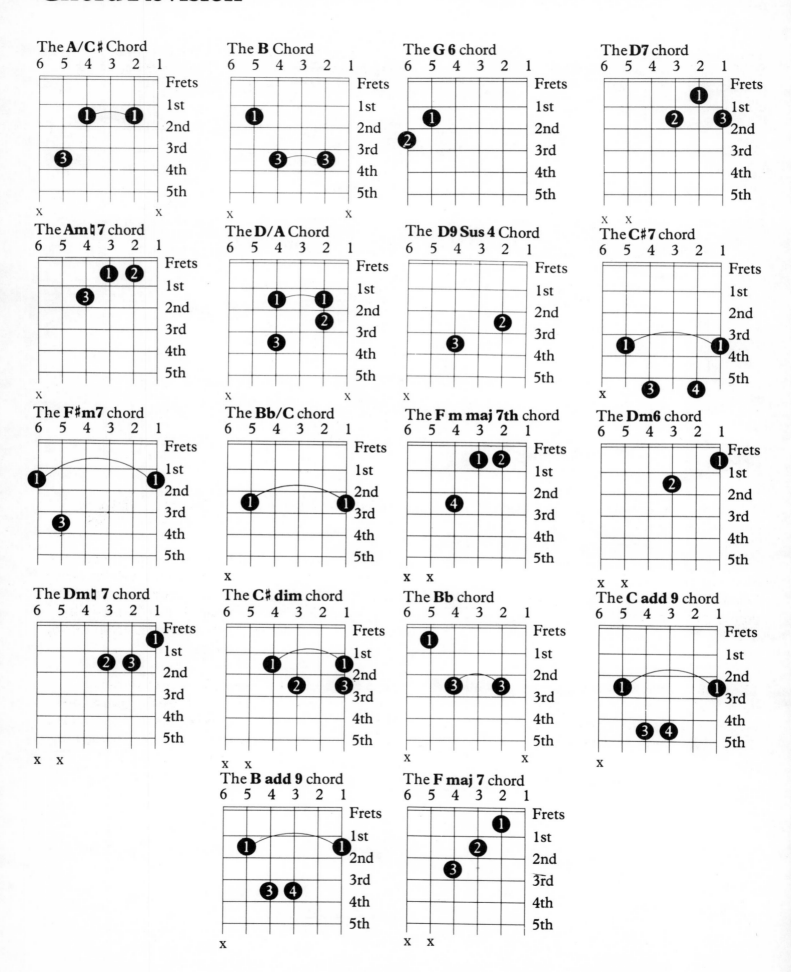

Just The Way You Are   Words & Music: Billy Joel

The **A minor 6** chord
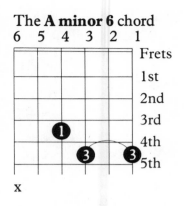

The **C seventh** chord
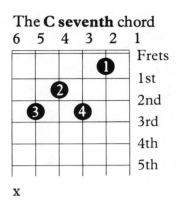

The **G minor 7** chord
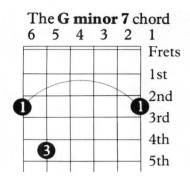

The **Ab** chord
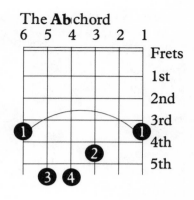

The **F minor 6** chord
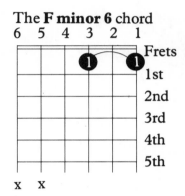

The **F minor 7** chord
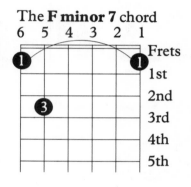

You will find the music for this romantic Billy Joel song on the following two pages. There are a few new chords to learn but only one new shape.

First look at the **Am6** diagram. This is a moveable four-string minor sixth shape, taking its name from the note stopped on the first string. In this case it is being used for **Am6,** so you can play the open A string as well.

The **Fm6** chord is the same shape moved four frets down the neck with the nut of the guitar taking the place of your first finger. Don't be confused by the fact that for **Fm6** the three string barré is fingered with the first finger and not the third. It just happens to be easier that way.

The **Ab** chord is self-explanatory and the minor sevenths are both played with the moveable six-string shape shown. These shapes take their name from the note stopped on the first string. (It could also take its name from the note stopped on the sixth string, it being the same note two octaves down.)

Finally, for this alternative **C7** we use a moveable shape that takes its name from the note stopped on the fifth string. Normally you would play only the inside four strings, but in this case you can play the top E as well, because that note is part of the **C7** chord.

Just The Way You Are Continued

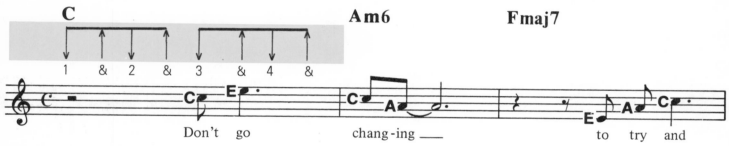

Don't go chang-ing ___ to try and

please me, ___ you ne-ver let me down ___ be-fore ___

mm ___ don't im-ag - ine ___ you're too fa-mil-

- iar ___ and I don't see ___ you ___ an - y

G7sus4   **G7**   **2, 4 Dm7**   **G7sus4**

- more. _____ I'll take you just ____ the way you are. __

C   **Fm6**   **C**   **F**   **G**

Fine

_____ I need to know __ that you __ will al-

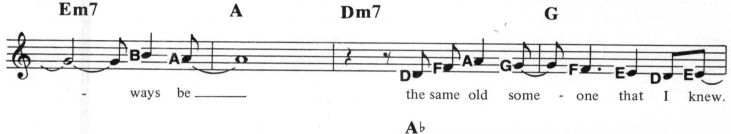

Em7   **A**   **Dm7**   **G**

- ways be _____ the same old some - one that I knew.

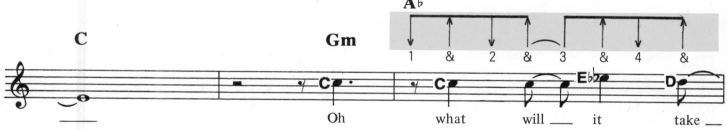

C   **Gm**   **A♭**

1 & 2 & 3 & 4 &

_____ Oh what will __ it take __

B♭   **Gm7**   **C7**

____ till you __ be - lieve _____ in me _____

D.C.(Repeat)

Fm7   **B♭**   **G7sus4**   **G7**

the way that I _____ be - lieve __ in you. _____

N.B. The full lyric for each song can be found at the back of the book.

Harmony Made Easy

A full explanation of modern harmony would completely fill this book. Set out here is an explanation of the harmonic structure of the chords you will find in this series and the reasons why they are given their names. Using the principles explained in this section you will be able to construct many new chords. For example, after learning how Cmaj7 is constructed you will be able to work out which notes make up any major seventh chord, and so on.

Harmony can be defined as the addition of different pitched notes to a melody, producing a series of chords. These chords progress, one to the other, and give a song its 'complete' feel. Harmony embellishes a melody played unaccompanied on a single note, which would not normally be thought of as complete.

Throughout these books, songs are presented as single note melodies with chord symbols above. It is these chord symbols which will now be presented in written notation, with explanations of why they are so called: All these examples are shown with a root C or A, but the same formations apply to any key, starting on the relevant root note.

Here is the scale of C major.

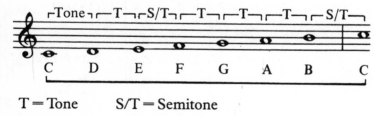

T = Tone   S/T = Semitone

You should remember from Book Two how the tones and semitones correspond to the frets on your guitar. Try building major scales starting on different notes. All you have to do is move up or across the neck using the same intervals shown above, i.e. T, T, S/T, T, T, T, S/T. In this way you can form *any* major scale. In the examples of chords that follow, the numbers indicate which position in the scale of Cmajor the notes occupy. Note that the eighth note of the scale is the same as the first or root note but it is 8 notes (12 semitones or one octave) higher. Similarly, when the notes continue into the next octave the ninth note is the same as the second, but an octave higher, and so on.

The notes which make up a chord can be arranged in almost any order, but some combinations sound better than others. These different formations of notes which make up chords are called inversions.

Notes which occur in a chord can be 'doubled' an octave higher or lower. For example, in your basic six string Emajor chord you will find three different E notes and two different B notes. Again, some combinations sound better than others.

Constructing chords on the guitar is sometimes a compromise owing to the physical limitations of trying to hold down six strings with four fingers. For this reason some notes in the guitar inversions of certain chords have been omitted. You will find, however, that these omissions do not alter the 'flavour' of the chord.

Major chords are based on what is called the major triad. This comprises the first, third and fifth notes of the major scale. To this triad you can make many additions which completely alter the sound of the chord. Here are examples of major chords you will find in this series of books:

Here is the basic Cmajor triad.

C (major)

Typical guitar inversion

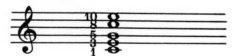

C7 (C seventh)

Typical Guitar Inversion

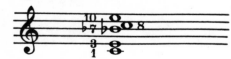

This chord could be called C flattened seventh, as you are adding the flattened (i.e. lowered by a semitone) seventh note of the scale.

There is a very good harmonic reason why this is so but it involves a long and complicated explanation. It is enough to say at this stage that when you see '7' after a chord the flattened seventh is added to the basic major triad.

Cmaj7 (C△7) (C major seventh)

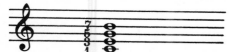

Typical Guitar Inversion

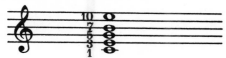

Here the seventh note of the major scale is added to the triad and it is therefore called C major seventh.

C+9 (C add 9)

Typical Guitar Inversion

For this chord the ninth note of the scale is added, it being exactly the same note (i.e. D) as the second note of the scale but an octave higher. The twelfth in the guitar inversion is similarly the fifth, an octave higher.

Cmaj9 (C△9) (C major ninth)

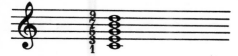

Typical Guitar Inversion

Here the ninth is added to the major seventh chord which was presented earlier. Note that the fifth can be omitted (as shown in the guitar inversion) without changing the 'flavour' of the chord.

C6 (C sixth)

Typical Guitar Inversion

Here the sixth is added to the triad. The fifth can be omitted as shown in the guitar inversion.

C7♭9 (C7-9) (C seven flat nine)

Typical Guitar Inversion

This chord is formed by adding a flattened ninth to the C seventh chord which has already been discussed. The seventh flat nine chord is very closely related to the diminished chord. In fact, you could substitute E diminished for C7♭9. You will understand why when we discuss diminished chords.

C7+ (C7 aug) (C seventh augmented)

Typical Guitar Inversion

The C seventh augmented is simply the basic C seventh with the fifth note of the scale raised or sharpened by a semitone.

Note the ♯12 in the guitar inversion is a ♯5 an octave up.

C7sus4 (C seventh suspended fourth)

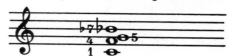

Typical Guitar Inversion

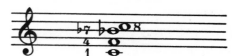

Suspended fourth chords contain the fourth note of the scale and no third. The fourth is said to be suspended because it does not belong in the chord and generally returns (resolves) to the third in following chords. For this reason sus 4 chords have an unfinished sound. C sus 4 is the same but it contains no (flattened) seventh.

Am is used for the minor chord examples as it is the relative minor to C major. It is so called because it has the same key signature.

Serious students should note that there are two forms of the minor scale and also that the melodic minor is different in its ascending and descending forms. All that it necessary, however, to understand the following section is to look at the:–

Ascending scale of 'A' melodic minor.

Note that all forms of the minor scale contain accidentals.

If you look back at the C major scale you will see that between the first and third notes there is a gap of tone, tone (T, T). This is called a major third.

Between the first and third notes of the minor scale you will see tone, semitone (T, S/T). This is called a minor third and gives minor chords what is often referred to as their 'sad sound'.

Just as the scale of C was used to show the construction of major chords, for this section you refer to the ascending scale of A melodic minor.

Here is the basic A minor triad.

Am (A minor)

Typical Guitar Inversion

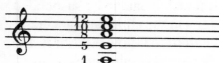

Note that the tenth note up the scale is the minor third an octave up.

Am7 (A minor seventh)

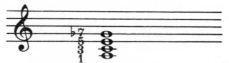

Typical Guitar Inversion

As with the seventh (7) chord in the major section, the seventh note of the scale is flattened (i.e. G♯ becomes G natural) and added to the triad.

Am6 (A minor sixth)

Typical Guitar Inversion

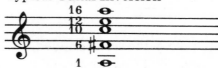

Here the sixth is added to the minor triad.

Am7♭5 (A minor seventh flat five)

Typical Guitar Inversion

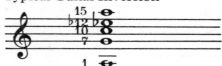

As with the major seventh chord in the major section, you add the seventh note of the scale to the minor triad.

To make this chord take Am7 and lower the fifth note a semitone (i.e. E becomes E♭).

Note that the ♭12 simply signifies the ♭5 has been moved an octave up.

C diminished
Shown for example as:– C° or Cdim

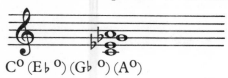

C° (E♭ °) (G♭ °) (A°)

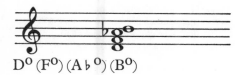

D° (F°) (A♭ °) (B°)

E° (G°)(B♭ °) (D♭ °)

Look at the first diminished chord. Working upwards from the root C you will find that all the notes are separated by a minor third. Now imagine the C has been taken up an octave and the root is now E♭. Working upwards again you find that all the notes are still separated by a minor third.

The same thing will happen no matter which note you use as the root.

This is a simplified explanation of why a diminished chord can take its name from any note included in the chord.

It was mentioned earlier that C 7-9 was closely related to E diminished. This is because the top four notes of the chord are exactly the same as E diminished. In fact, C 7-9 could be referred to as E diminished with a C in the base.

Rio

Moving on the floor now babe, you're a bird of paradise
Cherry ice cream smile I suppose it's very nice
With a step to your left and a flick to the right
You catch that mirror way out west
You know you're something special and you look like
    you're the best.

Chorus

Her name is Rio and she dances on the sand
Just like that river twisting through a dusty land
And when she shines, she really shows you all she can
Oh Rio, Rio, dance across the Rio Grande.

I've seen you on the beach and I've seen you on T.V.
Two of a billion stars, it means so much to me
Like a birthday or a pretty view
But then I'm sure that you know it's just for you.

Chorus

Hey now, look at that, did he nearly run you down?
At the end of the drive the lawmen arrive
You make me feel alive, alive, alive.
I'll take my chance 'cause luck is on my side
I tell you something, I know what you're thinking
I tell you something, I know what you're thinking.

Chorus (variation)

Her name is Rio and she dances on the sand
Just like that river twists across a dusty land
And when she shines she really shows you all she can
Oh Rio, Rio dance across the river Grande.

Her name is Rio she don't need to understand
And I might find her if I'm looking like I can.
Oh Rio, Rio hear them shout across the land
From mountains in the north down to the Rio Grande.

Without You

No, I can't forget this ev'ning
Or your face as you were leaving,
But I guess that's just the way the story goes.
You always smile but in your eyes your sorrow shows,
Yes, it shows.

No, I can't forget tomorrow
When I think of all my sorrow
And I had you there but then I let you go.
And now it's only fair that I should let you know
What you should know.

Chorus

I can't live, if living is without you,
I can't live, I can't give any more.
I can't live if living is without you,
I can't give, I can't give any more.

No, I can't forget this ev'ning
Or your face as you were leaving,
But I guess that's just the way the story goes.
You always smile but in your eyes your sorrow shows,
Yes, it shows.

Chorus.

Alright Now

There she stood in the street
Smiling from her head to her feet,
I said "Hey, what is this?"
Now baby, maybe she's in need of a kiss
I said "Hey, what's your name baby
Maybe we can see things the same
Now don't you wait or hesitate,
Let's move before they raise the parking rate."

Chorus

All right now
Baby, it's all right now.
All right now
Baby, it's all right now.

I took her home to my place
Watching every move on her face,
She said "Look, what's your game
Baby are you tryin' to put me in shame?"
I said "Slow, don't go so fast
Don't you think that love can last?"
She said "Love, Lord above,
Now you're tryin' to trick me in love."

Chorus

Goodbye Yellow Brick Road

When are you gonna come down,
When are you going to land
I should have stayed on the farm,
Should have listened to my old man.

So goodbye Yellow Brick Road
Where the dogs of society howl
You can't plant me in your penthouse,
I'm going back to my plough.
Back to the howling old owl in the woods,
Hunting the horny back toad.
Oh I've finally decided my future lies
Beyond the Yellow Brick Road.

You know you can't hold me forever,
I didn't sign up with you.
I'm not a present for your friends to open
The boys too young to be singing the blues.

What do you think you'll do then
I bet that'll shoot down your plane.
It'll take you a couple of vodka and tonics
To set you on your feet again.
Maybe you'll get a replacement,
There's plenty like me to be found.
Mongrels who ain't got a penny
Singing for titbits like you on the ground.

Tonight I Celebrate My Love

Tonight I celebrate my love for you,
It seems the natural thing to do.
Tonight no one's gonna find us,
We'll leave the world behind us
When I make love to you (tonight).
(Repeat)

Chorus

Tonight I celebrate my love for you
And the midnight sun is gonna come shining through
Tonight there'll be no distance between us
What I want most to do is to get close to you tonight.

Tonight I celebrate my love for you
And I hope that deep inside you feel it too.
Tonight our spirits will be climbing
To a sky lit up with diamonds
When I make love to you tonight.

Tonight I celebrate my love for you
And soon this old world will seem brand new.
Tonight we will both discover
How friends turn to lovers,
When I make love to you tonight.

Y.M.C.A.

Young man there's no need to feel down
I said young man pick yourself off the ground
I said young man 'cause you're in a new town
There's no need to be unhappy.
Young man there's a place you can go,
I said, young man when you're short on your dough
You can stay there and I'm sure you will find
Many ways to have a good time.

Chorus

It's fun to stay at the Y.M.C.A.
It's fun to stay at the Y.M.C.A.
They have everything for young men to enjoy
You can hang out with all the boys.
It's fun to stay at the Y.M.C.A.
It's fun to stay at the Y.M.C.A.
Get yourself clean, you can have a good meal,
You can do whatever you feel.

Young man, are you listening to me?
I said, young man what do you want to be?
I said, young man you can make real your dreams.
But you've got to know this one thing.
No man does it all by himself.
I said, young man put your pride on the shelf.
And just go there to the Y.M.C.A.
I'm sure they can help you today.

Young man I was once in your shoes
I said, I was down and out with the blues.
I felt no man cared if I were alive.
I felt the whole world was so jive.
That's when someone came up to me
And said, "Young man, take a walk up the street.
It's a place there called the Y.M.C.A.
They can start you back on your way."

Chorus (last half)

It's fun to stay at the Y.M.C.A.
It's fun to stay at the Y.M.C.A.
Young man, young man, there's no need to feel down,
Young man, young man, pick yourself off the ground.

I Just Called To Say I Love You

No New Year's day to celebrate
No chocolate covered candy hearts to give away
No first of spring, no song to sing,
In fact here's just another ordinary day.

No April rain, no flowers bloom
No wedding Saturday within the month of June.
But what it is is something true
Made up of these three words that I must say to you.

Chorus

I just called to say I love you
I just called to say how much I care
I just called to say I love you,
And I mean it from the bottom of my heart.

No summers high, no warm July
No harvest moon to light one tender August night
No autumn breeze, no falling leaves
Not even time for birds to fly to southern skies.

No Libra sun, no halloe'en
No giving thanks to all the Christmas joy you bring
But what it is, though old, so new
To fill your heart like no three words could ever do.

Chorus.

Bright Eyes

Is it a kind of dream floating out on the tide,
Following the river of death downstream
Oh is it a dream?

Is it a kind of shadow reaching in to the night
Wandering over the hills unseen
Or is it a dream?

There's a fog along the horizon a strange glow in the sky
And nobody seems to know where you go and what does
  it mean
Oh is it a dream?

There's a high wind in the trees a cold sound in the air
And nobody ever knows when you go and where do you
  start
Oh oh in to the dark.

Chorus

Bright eyes burning like fire
Bright eyes how can you close and fail
How can the light that burned so brightly
Suddenly burn so pale?
Bright eyes, bright eyes, bright eyes.

Going Down Town Tonight

I'm going down town tonight I'm gonna find myself a
  dream
I'm gonna dress up right and be the best they've ever
  seen.

You can tell from their eyes, you can tell from their eyes,
That they're never impressed, that they're never
  impressed,
From the way they walk round, from the way they walk
  round,
They are used to the best, oh, are used to the best.

I'm going down town tonight, I'm going down town
  tonight,
I'm going down town tonight, I'm going down town
  tonight.

Just one thing before you go, my ladies of the night
Just one thing I have to say, I've got you
And you're confident and debonair, you move between
  the stars
Hungry for those starving eyes that feed your waking hours.

Why let them break you with their self-sophisticated
  grace?
'Cause when the cards are low you see the smile come on
  their face.

If you speak the right words, if you speak the right words
They will hear what you say, oh will hear what you say
They will take your attention, just take your attention
And then turn away, oh and then turn away.

The place has all run dry with lonely echoes of the night
And some walk home alone while others find and hold
  on tight.

If you speak the right words, if you speak the right words
They will hear what you say, oh will hear what you say
They will take your attention, just take your attention
And then turn away, oh and then turn away.

Killing Me Softly With His Song

I heard he sang a good song; I heard he had a style.
And so I came to see him to listen for a while.
And there he was this young boy, a stranger to my eyes.

Chorus

Strumming my pain with his fingers
Singing my life with his words.
Killing me softly with his song,
Killing me softly with his song,
Telling my whole life with his words,
Killing me softly, with his song.

I felt all flushed with fever, embarrassed by the crowd
I felt he'd found my letters and read each one out loud
I prayed that he would finish but he just kept right on.

Chorus

He sang as if he knew me, in all my dark despair
And then he looked right through me as if I wasn't there
But he was there this stranger, singing clear and strong.

Chorus.

Hold Me Now

I have a picture pinned to my wall
An image of you and of me and we're laughing with love
  at it all.
Look at our life now tattered and torn,
We fuss and we fight and delight in the tears that we cry
  until dawn.

Chorus

Hold me now, oh warm my heart,
Stay with me, let lovin' start
Let lovin' start.

You say I'm a dreamer, we're two of a kind
Both of us searching for some perfect world we know
  we'll never find.
So perhaps I should leave here, go far away
But you know that there's nowhere that I'd rather be
  than with you here today.

You asked if I love you, what can I say?
You know that I do and that this is just one of those
  games that we play.
So I'll sing you a new song, please don't cry anymore
I'll even ask your forgiveness though I don't know just
  what I'm asking it for.

Chorus.

Knowing Me, Knowing You

No more carefree laughter
Silence ever after
Walking through an empty house
Tears in my eyes.
This is where the story ends,
This is goodbye.

Knowing me, knowing you,
There is nothing we can do,
Knowing me, knowing you,
We just have to face it,
This time we're through.

Breaking up is never easy I know
But I have to go.
Knowing me, knowing you,
It's the best I can do.

Memories, good days, bad days.
They'll be with me always.
In these old familiar rooms children would play
Now there's only emptiness, nothing to say.

Only You

Looking from a window above is like a story of love
Can you hear me?
   came back only yesterday, we're moving farther away,
Want you near me.

Chorus

All I needed was the love you gave
All I needed for another day,
And all I ever knew, only you.

Sometimes when I think of her name, when it's only a
   game
And I need you
Listen to the words that you say, it's getting harder to
   stay
When I see you.

This is gonna take a long time, and I wonder what's mine
Can't take no more
Wonder if you'll understand, it's just the touch of your
   hand
Behind closed door.

Easy Lover

Easy Lover,
She'll get a hold on you believe it,
She's like no other,
Before you know it you'll be on your knees.

She's an easy lover,
She'll take your heart but you won't feel it
She's like no other,
And I'm just trying to make you see.

She's the kind of girl you dream of
Dream of keeping hold of
Better forget it
You'll never get it.
She will play around and leave you
Leave you and deceive you
Better forget it
Oh you'll regret it.

You're the one that wants to hold her,
Hold her and control her,
Better forget it,
You'll never get it
'Cause she'll say that there's no other
Till she finds another.
Better forget it
Oh, you'll regret
And don't try to change her,
Just leave her, leave her
You're not the only one and seeing is believing
It's the only way you'll ever know.

No you'll never change her
So leave her, leave her
Get out quick
'Cause seeing is believing,
It's the only way you'll ever know.

She's an easy lover.
(Repeat & fade)

Just The Way You Are

Don't go changing, to try and please me,
You never let me down before,
Mm, don't imagine you're too familiar
And I don't see you any more.

I wouldn't leave you, in times of trouble,
We never could have come this far
Mm, I took the good times, I'll take the bad times
I'll take you just the way you are.

I need to know that you will always be
The same old someone that I knew.
Oh what will it take till you believe in me,
The way that I believe in you?

Don't go trying some new fashion
Don't change the colour of your hair mm mm
You always have my unspoken passion
Although I might not seem to care.

I don't want clever conversation
I never want to work that hard, mm mm
I just want someone that I can talk to
I want you just the way you are.

I said I love you, and that's forever
And this I promise from the heart, mm mm
I could not love you any better
I love you just the way you are.

Exclusive Distributors:
Music Sales Limited
8/9 Frith Street, London W1V 5TZ, England.

Music Sales Pty Limited
120 Rothschild Avenue, Rosebery, NSW 2018, Australia.

This book © Copyright 1985, 1994 by Wise Publications
Order No. AM60575
ISBN 0-7119-0758-7

Art direction by Mike Bell.
Assisted by Lynda Hassett.
Designed by Sands Straker Limited.
Photography by Peter Wood.
Fender guitar supplied by Soho Sound House.
Arranged by Roger Day.
Music processed by Music Print Limited.

Music Sales' complete catalogue describes thousands of titles and is available in
full colour sections by subject, direct from Music Sales Limited.
Please state your areas of interest and send a cheque/postal order for £1.50 for postage to:
Music Sales Limited, Newmarket Road, Bury St. Edmunds, Suffolk IP33 3YB.

Printed in the United Kingdom by
Redwood Books, Trowbridge, Wiltshire.

New from Music Sales - the one-and only, ultimate busker book! It's *the* book to take to a party... to a gig... on your holiday... or to that famous desert island!

It's packed with literally hundreds and hundreds of the best-loved songs of all time... from vintage standards of the 30s right through to the latest pop hits.

"The Suitcase Book"!

"Probably the best songbook in the world."

The Busker's Fake Book 1001 All-Time Hit Songs

"The only songbook you'll ever need!"

For piano, organ, guitar, all electronic keyboards and all 'C' instruments. With an easy-to-use A-Z title finder plus a classified 'song type' index.
As a taster, here's just a quarter of the titles in this unique bumper songbook...

'A' You're Adorable
A Fine Romance
A Fool Such As I
A Hard Day's Night
A Man And A Woman
A Teenager In Love
Act Naturally
Against All Odds
Ain't Misbehavin'
All I Have To Do Is Dream
All My Loving
America
An American In Paris
An Old Fashioned Love Song
Angel Eyes
Another Suitcase In Another Hall
As Time Goes By
Band On The Run
Barbara Ann
Baubles Bangles And Beads
Because
Bennie And The Jets
Big Girls Don't Cry
Big Spender
Bird Dog
Blowin' In The Wind
Boogie Woogie Bugle Boy
Buffalo Gals
Bye Bye Love
California Dreaming
Can't Smile Without You
Candle In The Wind
Caravan
Chantilly Lace
Come Fly With Me
Consider Yourself
Crazy
Cruising Down The River
Dancing Queen
Daniel
Desafinado
Devil In Disguise
Diamonds Are A Girl's Best Friend
Do You Know The Way To San Jose
Don't Cry For Me Argentina
Don't Pay The Ferryman
Don't Sleep In The Subway
EastEnders
Ebony And Ivory
Eleanor Rigby
Empty Chairs At Empty Tables
The Entertainer
Every Breath You Take
First Time Ever I Saw Your Face
Fools Rush In
From Me To You
Funiculi, Funicula
Für Elise
Get Back
Get It On (Bang A Gong)
The Girl From Ipanema
Good Vibrations
Goodbye Yellow Brick Road
Guys And Dolls
Happy Xmas (War Is Over)
Havah Nagilah
He Ain't Heavy He's My Brother
Hello Mary Lou

Hello, Goodbye
Here, There And Everywhere
Hey Jude
Hey, Good Lookin'
Honeysuckle Rose
I Came I Saw I Conga'd
I Don't Want To Spoil The Party
I Dreamed A Dream
I Feel Pretty
I Fought The Law
I Left My Heart In San Francisco
I Saw Her Standing There
I'm A Loser
I'm Beginning To See The Light
I'm Still Standing
If I Had A Hammer
If I Were A Bell
In The Air Tonight
It Never Rains In Southern California
It's Not Unusual
It's So Easy
Jambalaya
Jealous Guy
La Ronde De l'Amour
Lady D'Arbanville
The Lady In Red
The Lambeth Walk
The Last Time I Saw Paris
Layla
Leaning On A Lamp Post
Let It Be
Let's Twist Again
The Lion Sleeps Tonight
Live And Let Die
Long Tall Sally
Love And Marriage
Lover Man
Lucille
Luck Be A Lady
Lullaby Of Birdland
Maple Leaf Rag
Maria
Me And My Girl
Mister Bojangles
Money For Nothing
Mull Of Kintyre
Never On A Sunday
Nights In White Satin
Norwegian Wood
Not Fade Away
O Sole Mio
Oh, Pretty Woman
Ol' Man River
On A Slow Boat To China
Only The Lonely
P.S. I Love You
Peggy Sue
Pennies From Heaven
Penny Lane
Pigalle
Poison Ivy
The Power Of Love
Raindrops Keep Falling On My Head
Rave On
Rhapsody In Blue
Riders On The Storm
Rock Around The Clock

Ruby Don't Take Your Love To Town
Satin Doll
Scarborough Fair
Shake Rattle And Roll
She Loves You
Singing The Blues
Sixteen Tons
Sloop John B
Smoke Gets In Your Eyes
Solitude
Something
Somewhere
Spanish Eyes
Standing On The Corner
Stars Fell On Alabama
Stranger In Paradise
Strangers In The Night
Streets Of London
Sugarbush
Sultans Of Swing
Summertime Blues
Sunshine Of Your Love
Sweet Charity
Swing Low, Sweet Chariot
Take Back Your Mink
Take That Look Off Your Face
Take The 'A' Train
Teen Angel
The Tender Trap
That'll Be The Day
Theme For A Dream
These Foolish Things
They Didn't Believe Me
This Guy's In Love With You
This Land Is Your Land
Those Were The Days
Three Little Fishies
Till There Was You
To Know Him Is To Love Him
Tonight
True Love Ways
Tulips From Amsterdam
Tutti Frutti
Unchained Melody
Under The Boardwalk
Up, Up And Away
Uptown Girl
The Very Thought Of You
Wake Up Little Susie
Walk Tall
The Way You Look Tonight
We Can Work It Out
We Don't Need Another Hero
We Shall Overcome
We'll Meet Again
What Kind Of Fool Am I
Wheels
When I'm Sixty Four
When Irish Eyes Are Smiling
When This Lousy War Is Over
Where Have All The Flowers Gone
Witchcraft
With A Little Help From My Friends
Woman
Yellow Submarine
Yesterday
Your Cheatin' Heart
Your Song

Melody, lyrics and guitar chords to literally hundreds and hundreds of the best songs of all time... from the golden standards through to the great pop hits of today.

Wise Publications
Order No. AM12345

While compiling this huge book, editor/arranger Peter Lavender kept all the artwork in a huge suitcase! But now that it's printed, this new mega-bumper busker book is a lot easier to carry around!

Surprisingly portable, in fact, at the usual songbook size of 12" x 9"... with some 656 pages!

As well as the 1,001 songs, the book includes a handy A-Z alphabetical title index *and* a classified index, too.